Great
Is the Company

ILLUSTRATIONS BY RAFAEL PALACIOS

Revised Edition 1953

Great
Is the Company

BY VIOLET WOOD

X655

FRIENDSHIP PRESS ✳ NEW YORK

Library of Congress Catalog Card Number: 53-9344

For my mother

Acknowledgments

I WISH to express appreciation to Margaret T. Hills, Associate in the Translations Department and Librarian of the American Bible Society, for sharing her amazing knowledge of the Bible, giving unstintingly of her time in problems of research, making available the resources of the library, and acting as historical adviser for this publication; to Dr. Francis C. Stifler, American Bible Society Secretary of Public Relations, for gracious permission to expand and dramatize some of the ideas and stories used in his radio broadcasts and for many constructive suggestions as an editorial reader of the manuscript; to biographers and historians of the past and present, as well as to those missionary-translators and archeologists who published journals, autobiographies, and other documents, for the factual material and historical data on which the stories appearing in this book are founded.

VIOLET WOOD

Champaign-Urbana, Illinois
March, 1953

Contents

1

The World's Imperishable Treasure

TWENTY years is a long time for a man to live a lie, and Don Cornelio had all but forgotten he was a professional liar. He had come to consider himself an artist. He enjoyed the fear and awe with which men looked at him, and he took pride in the number of simple people in each village whom he could hoodwink and dazzle. He boasted to his cronies that he could spellbind any audience in any village of Central America, and his boast was no idle gesture.

Don Cornelio practiced witchcraft. By the manipulation of his facial muscles, the use of ventriloquism, and the optical illusions his sleight of hand created, he convinced many a trusting soul that none equaled him in the realm of black magic. People eagerly bought his books of evil incantations. Girls drank the potions that, he assured them, would enable them to win the love of some indifferent boy. His formulas were sought by men who wished to put a curse upon their enemies. For almost twenty years Cornelio and his wife had made a handsome living out of their show and from the sale of worthless twigs and herbs with so-called magic powers.

Cornelio stopped at nothing. He went one day to a station of the Central American Mission, curious to see what kind of performance would attract so many people. Impressed by the effects of the preaching on the people, but personally quite untouched by it, he bought one of the Bibles. His easy smile and his well timed questions deceived the missionary, who thought he had an honest inquirer. Cornelio wanted only to find out how he could turn the divinations of this seemingly powerful book to his own profit.

For four months as he traveled about the country, Cornelio read his Bible with increasing devotion and growing interest. The trial of Jesus absorbed him, and he kept his wife awake many a night telling her the story as the meaning unfolded itself to him. The hours of failure and the days of grandeur of men like David and Paul haunted him. Only after his hands began to betray him and he fumbled some of his routine tricks on stage did he realize something was happening to him.

His eyes sweeping over an audience did not now estimate how much of a take he was likely to get. He saw before him the upturned faces of lonely, fearful, betrayed, and heartsick men and women. He looked at them and seemed to see Job and Mary Magdalene in their midst. From what he learned of family affairs, he found Joseph and Ruth among the throng. He saw himself all too clearly as the priest and the Levite who by-passed the abandoned victim on the Jericho road.

Cornelio found himself stuttering over the glib sales talk calculated to overcome a poor girl's doubts about the expensive love potions he was peddling. Thinking of the two great commandments of Jesus, he gave new counsel to men who came to him to buy a curse. "Go instead," he would advise, "and come to an understanding with your brother."

Sales dropped off, and Cornelio's wife was frightened. "It's that book you've got your head in day and night."

"Yes," said Cornelio, "it is the book. But until I have read it all, I will not put it by."

The night Cornelio discovered the message of Peter, "You have been born anew, not of perishable seed but of imperishable, through the living and abiding word of God," he canceled his show. He read on, "So put away all malice and all guile and insincerity and envy and all slander," and determined to lay aside all these. Seeking someone who would understand and rejoice with him, he traveled back to the missionary who had sold him the book. "I have found my Saviour," Cornelio said simply.

For several months Cornelio continued to travel his old circuit. Now, however, his performance was no bag of tricks. It was a humble confession, from the platform, that he had been a swindler and a cheat. In each village he bought and burned publicly all the black magic books that he could find. Telling the people of the change that had come into his life, he offered them the book wherein lay their salvation, too. Today Cornelio is one of the most successful of that international brotherhood of "Blessed Book Agents," colporteurs who yearly distribute thousands of copies of the Bible to villagers all around the world.

The book that changed Cornelio's life has an age-long history and romance that no other book can equal. To no other book have so great a company of men and women devoted their lives, eager that thousands like Cornelio in every continent might know its message in their own tongue. Other books that achieve great fame are translated at most into a score of languages. The Bible or some part of it has been translated into 1,059 tongues. Other books are considered phenomenal when their sales in one country run for a year or two into a few million copies. The Bible in whole or in part has been the world's best-seller every year since the advent of the printed word. It now rolls off the presses at the rate of thirty million copies a year.

How this book has survived is a miracle. It is so old and revered that thousands of books have been published to give us knowledge about who wrote it and what it means. Theologians, anthropologists, poets, historians, and psychologists give us many weighty reasons for its survival, but man's belief that the Bible is the Word of God is the best explanation of all. To men and women of three great faiths, Jewish, Roman Catholic, and Protestant, the Bible

4

—in part for the Jews and in its entirety for the Roman Catholics and Protestants—is indeed the Word of God.

This Word was recorded by men, but our knowledge as to who these writers were, how many there were, and exactly when they wrote is incomplete. It is estimated by scholars that the writing down of the Old Testament took place over a period of one thousand years, from 1150 B.C. to 150 B.C. and that the New Testament was written during the century between A.D. 50 and A.D. 150. It was, of course, impossible for all writers who took part in this recording to know one another. They not only lived in thirteen different centuries, they spoke different tongues and came from many walks of life. David and Solomon were kings, Peter a lowly fisherman. Ezekiel was a priest, Amos a shepherd and dresser of sycamore trees.

The laws that the book of *Exodus* tells us God gave to Moses for an agricultural people thousands of years ago have had a profound influence on the laws of industrial civilizations. David's ancient song of the Shepherd Lord is still the world's greatest poem about God. Paul's passionate letter to the people of Corinth, asking them above all things to love one another, lives to be read and preached in the churches of nations unborn when he was alive.

The Ten Commandments and other laws given to Moses on Mt. Sinai were passed on by word of mouth from rabbi-teacher to rabbi-student, from father to son. When the Old Testament was finally written down in Hebrew, rolls of leather and papyrus scrolls were used. These traveled with the exiled Jews to other lands. Rabbis kept up the tradition of memorizing whole books in order to save the precious scrolls from wear and tear by use and so that they might be ready to write the words down again from memory should fire or flood destroy their precious copies. By the time the New Testament was completed, a change had taken place in the appearance of manuscripts. Instead of rolled scrolls, the codex form appeared. That is, collections of leaves were stacked one on top of the other, folded, and sewed together down the center— the pattern of our books today.

From the time of the first writing on papyrus until Johann Gutenberg invented printing from movable type, every time a Bible was made nearly 800,000 words had to be copied by hand. The love and devotion of the minds of monks as well as the skill of their hands went into the making of every single copy. So far as is known, no part of the first manuscript of any book of the Bible is in existence. But the copies made and remade so faithfully from those original texts have never perished because men found in them universal truth and were willing to die that it might live.

What is in the Bible? We can be literal and say it is composed of sixty-six books, thirty-nine in the Old Testament and twenty-seven in the New. In these Testaments are letters, speeches, poems, hymns, dramas, laws and amendments to laws, historic documents, and stories, all hallowed by antiquity. We can say that here is an age-long diary recording the search of man for an understanding of God, an immortal textbook to instruct us in his ways. We can say the Bible is the record of a people crying out to heaven for a Messiah and biographies of that Messiah, Jesus, when he came to earth. We can say the Bible is a book whose pages speak of God and point generation after generation to Jesus Christ, "the Way and the Truth and the Life."

Whatever we say about the Bible, it is our own, a monumental heritage, a guide for our lives. If we fail to seek its wisdom, to know its beauty, and to follow its truth, we sell our birthright, an inheritance of singing power that would enrich our personal lives as it has endowed our civilization.

Our daily speech is infiltrated with allusions to biblical characters and themes. When we say, "poor as Job," "a doubting Thomas," "bricks without straw," "salt of the earth," "the apple of his eye," we borrow from the Bible. The titles of more than a thousand of our modern novels, plays, and motion pictures have been dipped from the creative fountain of the Bible. Examples are *Young Lions* and *Voice of the Turtle*.

The Bible has indeed fulfilled the psalmist's testimony, "Thy word is a lamp." Down through dark centuries and across blighted continents its wisdom, sought and followed as it has always been by great men and women, has helped to keep the lamp of civilization burning.

In the New York City Public Library reference room, the Bible is often called for. All of the many copies are thumb-scarred in identical spots—the Christmas story in *Luke*, the Sermon on the Mount in *Matthew*, the poetry of *Psalms*, the drama of *Job*, the fourteenth chapter of *John*, and other passages that speak to the varied needs of men. The possession of this truth for many centuries in the hearts of men of both the East and West has made the revelations of this book a consecrated knowledge.

7

The Bible has endured despite the death penalty for reading, translating, or possessing it threatened at various times in the Roman Empire, England, China, Madagascar, Spain, and other corners of the world. On the issue of giving common access to the Bible, the Protestant faith was built. Out of a passion for living by the Word of God, the Pilgrim Fathers fled England and laid the cornerstone of what was to become the United States of America.

The Bible has inspired thousands of missionaries to leave their homes and to devote years of laboring in strange lands. Often they found no written language for the strange tongues they had to learn to speak. With the help of nationals in many a country, missionaries have built the sound of a spoken language into an alphabet, compiled a dictionary, prepared a grammar, and finally translated the entire Bible into a new tongue. This desire and sacrificial willingness to share the Bible with others has opened the door in many countries to a new civilization and culture. This missionary eagerness of Christians to tell others about the love of God and the teachings of his Son has opened a way for men of all nations and races to live as brothers.

Great indeed is the company of those who labored to record the Word of God. Equally great has been the company of men and women who have preserved and translated the Bible from its first appearance to the present day. They are the heroes of our story. Through their lives we shall discover the place of the Bible in the molding of religion, law, music, art, and literature and in the making of men and nations.

2

Breaking
the Barrier of Language

THE man, Jerome, was the talk of the town. The time of all this talk was A.D. 382, the town in which it took place, Rome. The man we call St. Jerome today had then the sobering name of Eusebius Sophronius Hieronymus. It was rumored that none was closer to Pope Damasus, and after an acquaintance of only a few weeks, too.

Monks meeting on the streets asked each other, "Did you know that this Jerome has traveled the length and breadth of Greece?" And another would retort, "That's nothing. I have it that he's been to the Grotto of the Nativity in Bethlehem." Students who clamored to attend Jerome's lectures on Scripture, which Pope Damasus had speedily made it possible for him to give, asked, "Is it really true that when he can't buy copies of rare old manuscripts, he makes his own? Whether they be in Greek or Latin or Hebrew?" And pagan ladies, riding in slave-borne litters through the streets of Rome, frequently stopped to stare boldly at the proud and haunting figure of Jerome.

For his first audience with the pope, Jerome had dressed as humbly as always. He wore the coarsest of ankle-length robes, corded about the middle of his tall, emaciated figure. The skin that stretched tensely over the bony frame of his face and hands was rough and black from a three-year-long exposure to the desert sun and sands of Chalcis, where he had studied and done penance as a religious hermit.

The pope's dismay at the appearance of this austere monk gave way to admiration and delight in him as they talked Scripture together. Here was a biblical scholar second to none. The pope rejoiced in Jerome and invited him back day after day. Their informal talks were often interrupted by the arrival of bishops of the Eastern Churches. These dignitaries were pouring into Rome from Greece, Syria, Egypt, Constantinople, and Jerusalem to greet the pope and to be on hand for the coming meeting of the Council of Churches. The pope's amazement was unbounded as he watched these foreign bishops embrace Jerome. The man had apparently been everywhere; he seemed to know and be known by all.

The pope, who had not yet appointed the secretary for the Council meeting, knew that he had been waiting for just such a man as Jerome. This first papal task Jerome fulfilled well. Pope Damasus next appointed Jerome as the secretary of the papacy and then commissioned him to translate the *Psalms* and the New Testament from Greek into Latin. Jerome took three years to make this translation. During these years he also acted as scriptural consultant to the pope and taught classes of young men and, what was quite revolutionary, young women, some of them wealthy pagans.

Principal among these women was Marcella, a distinguished patrician widow who gave up her luxurious silk gowns, her slaves, and even her palace on the Aventine to become a Christian. She turned part of her palace into a retreat devoted to works of mercy among the poor. The rest of it was used as a school for the training of other wealthy women so that they might learn from Jerome, as she had, the Christian way of service.

People talked about the change in Marcella. They thought it was terrible. Christian scholarship, prayer and fasting, the pursuit of a holy life, and the wearing of long, black robes were strictly the province of men. The poor and the sick, however, blessed the names of Jerome and Marcella from one end of the Eternal City to the other. Soon other women, like the rich and influential widow Paula and her daughters, Blesilla and Eustochium, also came to Jerome's lectures.

Jerome and Marcella did not realize it, but the palace on the Aventine, which Jerome renamed the "Church of the Household," was really the first convent. It was also the beginning of the long history of Christian hospitals and asylums.

When Damasus died, there was a move to make Jerome pope, but the scheme failed. Later the new pope became so jealous of Jerome's learning and influence that Jerome feared to remain in Rome. He gave much thought to where he would settle, for a great plan was stirring in his mind.

Jerome wished to become so proficient in the use of Hebrew that he might also translate the Old Testament into Latin. "And where better might I go," he asked his dismayed Church of the Household, "than to the Holy Land itself?" Jerome went then to Bethlehem.

His action, however, caught hold of the imagination of the students and workers whom he had left in Rome. Shortly after, all of Roman society was again wagging its tongue, this time over the band of pilgrims who followed Jerome to Bethlehem. These were men and women from among Jerome's converts, led by Paula and her two daughters. In Bethlehem, Paula gave up her entire fortune to the building of a church, a house for the monks, a house for the women, and a "hospice" for the sheltering of the hordes of pilgrims who had begun to come from all over the world to visit the Holy Land.

For thirty-four years Jerome lived in Bethlehem administering the affairs of this monastery. He also studied and wrote, producing twenty-four books of biblical commentaries, a group of "hermit biographies," two histories of the early church, and many treatises.

But none of these achievements, nor all of them together, compares with one single work for which his name has been remembered in the realm of scholarship for nearly sixteen hundred years—the translation of the Bible into Latin. To Jerome translation of the Bible was a stupendous task for which the days were never long enough. During many a week of inspiration, Jerome slept less than most men sleep in a single night.

He was assisted in copying and in word study by the men and women of the Church of the Household. As Paula's knowledge of classical languages increased, she devoted more and more of her time to the task of translation. It was, however, Jerome's unflagging spirit that kept the work going decade after decade. Every word was written by hand. Certain pages were revised and edited and recopied scores of times until they satisfied their translator. The books of *Samuel* and *Kings* appeared first. When these were circulated and the bishops of the churches of the West learned what Jerome was doing, jealousy prompted them to accuse him of tampering with the Word of God. He was charged with using the translation to put across his own ideas. So far as is known, this was the first time, but by no means the last, that a biblical translator or reviser was to suffer such accusations.

Jerome was acutely sensitive on the score of the intellectual honesty of his translation. He wrote of such attacks, "If my occupation had been to plait rush baskets or to weave mats out of palm leaves, in order, by the sweat of my brow, to gain my daily bread, envy would have spared me. But since in obedience to the precepts of the Saviour, I have, for the good of souls, chosen to prepare the bread which perishes not and have wished to clear the path of truth of the weeds which ignorance has sown in it,

I am accused of a two-fold crime. If I correct errors in the Sacred Text, I am denounced as a falsifier; if I do not correct them, I am pilloried as a disseminator of error."

The translation of the Bible was the main work done in the Bethlehem monastery. Here devoted Christians copied manuscripts in rooms that came to be called "scriptoria." Following the example of Jerome's group, generations of Benedictine, Franciscan, and Dominican monks and nuns labored night and day in their lonely cells, copying and preserving by hand the books of the Bible. Often with great beauty they performed works of art on the opening letter of each chapter, which we call "illuminated letters," and sometimes added larger decorations and illustrations. If it had not been for the zeal and devotion of these religious copyists in the scriptoria, many of the world's oldest literary treasures, including the Bible, would have been lost to us.

Jerome grew old in the performance of the task of translation. The day came when his eyesight failed, but the lamps still burned in his monastic study. Young monks read aloud to him the letters from the Hebrew scrolls that his eyes were no longer able to decipher. He would then dictate the translation in Latin to other young monks, and so the work went on. It was completed in A.D. 405 when Jerome was seventy-five years old. The translation of the Old Testament was combined with his earlier translation of the New, and they appeared together for the first time in history. This Bible came to be called the Vulgate (from the Latin word *vulgatus,* meaning common or usual) because of its common use by churchmen. It was later adopted as the authorized version of the entire church. The Vulgate is today still used as the authentic Latin version of the Bible by scholars in the Roman Catholic Church.

Whenever a council of the church convened, the Vulgate was carried in triumph in a golden reliquary. "Our ancestors," the historian Ozaman said, "had good reason to cover it with gold. For this first of ancient books is also the first of modern books; from its pages have sprung all the languages, all the eloquence, all the civilization of the centuries."

His name was Dr. John Wycliffe, but they called him anything but that. They called him "Doctor Wicked-Believe," "Flatteries Sinke," "Lying Glutton," "Devells Instrument," in fact a whole dictionary of bold and ribald names. They hauled him into court off and on for ten years. They chased his friends out of the country and hanged and quartered some of his followers. When his physicians announced he was going to die, his enemies sent a delegation of friars and a doctor of divinity who cheerfully threatened him with hell if he did not recant. He got so angry he recovered and lived another six years. Twenty-four years after his death they searched homes and schools for his books and tracts, which they burned publicly by the bushel basketful. Forty-four years after his burial they dug up his bones, burned them, and threw them into the river as a public spectacle "to the damnation and destruction of his memory." Was he a criminal, a fiend, a murderer of little children? No, his "crime" was daring to translate the Word of God into English.

Certainly no man's enemies talked more wildly or worked longer to discredit his life and work than those of John Wycliffe. But no man's enemies ever failed more miserably, for history has accorded him so bright a place in the pattern of progress that he is known today as "The Morning Star of the Reformation."

To know who these enemies were and how they came to be his enemies we have to know something of the England in which John Wycliffe lived from 1320 to 1384. It was an England that spoke the thick, sweet idiom of Chaucer. An England whose church and aristocracy were overburdened by the taxation of the pope for the glory of Rome. An England whose people were mostly serfs. An England where, because of highwaymen, two out of every ten travelers never got to their destination unscathed. An England where most of the priesthood from friar to cardinal were so degenerate that their preachments were little more than anecdotes from the lives of the saints.

John Wycliffe made the church authorities, from the pope down to the friars, and many of the aristocracy as well, his enemies because he wanted to change things. He had a passionate belief that the church, in departing from the authority of the Bible, was far from Christian in practice. As a teacher of theology at Oxford, he knew his Bible, and as a priest of the church in Lutterworth, he knew his people. He believed that if the common people knew what was in the Bible, their lives would be enriched. With the Bible's revelation of God in their hearts and minds, they could then judge for themselves the pope's edicts and the friars' behavior. But to suggest that people think for themselves on religious matters was heresy! It was the clergy's job to tell the people what to think!

Great obstacles stood in the way of this brave man's theory. One was that the Bible did not exist in English. When read in the churches, if at all, it was read in Latin, which nobody understood. The second obstacle was that the serfs and peasants of England were illiterate. Even if the Bible had existed in English, the majority of the people would not have been able to read it.

Wycliffe was never a man to avoid the risks of a prophecy. He said, in effect, "Give the people the Book and I predict they will learn to read and will be born again. Until they learn to read, let them hear, at least, the message of the sacredness of the individual in the eyes of God. Then and only then will they stir themselves on the issue of their freedom and education and act on it religiously, politically, and socially." Which was exactly why the name of Wycliffe was a red flag to most of the clergy and the aristocracy of that time! They had no intention of letting their serfs learn to read the Bible, to worship God in their own way, and to revolt!

To overcome that first obstacle, Wycliffe, in 1379, gathered about him a group of Oxford scholars like Dr. John Purvey and rebellious priests like Nicholas de Hereford. Together they started the translation of the Latin Vulgate into English. It was a good thing that Wycliffe did not wait for the completion of the translation before beginning to circulate it, for he died three years before it was finished by John Purvey. As each portion was translated, Wycliffe had caused hundreds of copies of it, all made by hand, to be broadcast among the people who could read.

In order to circulate knowledge of the Book among the nonreading public, Wycliffe formed a group called "poor priests." The art of the period depicts the poor priest as dressed in a coarse brown robe, wearing a broad-brimmed hat and sandals and carrying a Bible and a walking staff. They traveled from door to door across rural England spreading Bible truths. They read the Bible aloud, and the English peasants eagerly memorized great portions of it.

What a contrast these poor priests must have seemed to the peasants who knew only the yearly visits of the bishops at the front gate of the estates to collect church fees from the noblemen and themselves! These bishops came in gay carriages, richly robed and hatted and surrounded by a retinue of servants. So great was the influence of the poor priests on the serfs that Wycliffe was accused of complicity in the Peasants' Revolt of 1381. While this revolt accomplished nothing in itself, it was the first uprising of any great number of peasants and the beginning of the end of the feudal system.

To give further guidance to the new Christians, Wycliffe instructed his poor priests in the organization of "conventicles," public gatherings in village squares and city meeting places. These prayerful gatherings were actually the forerunners of the town meetings the Pilgrims were to inaugurate in New England nearly three centuries later. Like everything Wycliffe thought of and carried out, the conventicles produced a storm of protest and a flood of papal letters and name-calling. The people had no right to public discussion of how they should worship God or what the Bible meant—that was the exclusive province of the pope and the clergy!

But there must have been many educated men on Wycliffe's side. Many hundreds of copies of the Wycliffe Bible must have been made in secret by the willing hands of the famous university men and priests of that day. This can be conjectured from the fact that, in spite of the seizing and wholesale burning of these Bibles in 1410 and again in 1413, one hundred and seventy manuscript copies of the Wycliffe Bible are still in existence.

By translating the Bible into English and by organizing the poor priests to teach it to the people, Wycliffe did overcome the great obstacles that stood between them and the Bible. And the people, once they had the Bible, were helped to overcome other obstacles that stood between them and freedom.

Before the era of the poor priests and their Book, an Englishman could travel twelve miles from one village to another and find Englishmen whose words were as strange to him as if they had been in a foreign language. In making his translation Wycliffe had pulled together the key words from England's nearly two hundred dialects. It was the words of this Bible, alive on the tongues of the English natives throughout England, that began the molding of their speech into a unified national language.

Wycliffe spread wide the pages of the Bible, and try as the authorities would to slam shut that Book, the people clamored for it. The words of the Bible gave the English peasants their first vision of themselves as free men. It nurtured them in the vocabulary of resistance. It changed their language and their history. The Bible was, as Thomas Huxley, the English scientist, has described it, "the Magna Charta of the poor and oppressed."

As a punishment for their work on this Bible, Purvey and Hereford were imprisoned and persecuted. Lord Cobham, who had helped finance their work, died at the stake. During his trial for "obstinate heresy" Lord Cobham said, "Before God and man I profess solemnly here that I never abstained from sin until I knew Wycliffe, whom ye so much disdain." John Huss, who carried into Bohemia the Wycliffe ideal of making the Bible accessible to the common man, was burned for heresy.

By 1415 England was in a terrible state of religious and political upheaval. So much of this confusion was laid at the door of the Bible that the law of the land decreed "the forefeit of land, catel, lif, and goods from their heyers forever" from any man caught reading the Bible in English.

What happens today when a book is censored? People go to great lengths to read it. This same thing happened in England in the fifteenth century. Men taught themselves and each other to read so that they might find out for themselves what was in the forbidden Book. What they found, as Wycliffe had prophesied, did, in time, help to make them free of popery and serfdom.

❀ ❀ ❀

The butcher and his young apprentice eyed each other furtively as the shop bell jangled admitting the burly-looking scholar.

"It is the mad professor who ordered the six sheep a week Monday," the butcher said out of the corner of his mouth.

"*Guten morgen!*" The professor had a booming voice. "I trust you have the sheep?"

The butcher nodded and beckoned him to follow.

The bleak patience in the blue eyes of the butcher boy changed to alert terror as the professor, in passing through the shop, rested his hand briefly on the boy's head. Not until they had gone through the door that the butcher carefully left ajar did the boy move. Then he tiptoed after them to stand peering through the narrow slit of the door leading to the slaughter house beyond.

Out of his cloth bag the professor brought a writing tablet, a great quill pen, a bottle of ink, and a sand box and set them carefully on the counting table. The butcher had begun his grisly work. The professor flinched at the eerie bleat of the struggling animal. The familiar job of slitting and dressing went on and on. The professor watched, then asked so suddenly that the boy jumped, "What is the word for that?" The boy knew then that the professor was indeed mad. Any child on the streets of Wittenberg could tell a sheep's kidney when he saw one!

The master worked fast, interrupted constantly by the professor asking foolish questions. It was clear he did not know a liver from a heart, nor a heart from a lung— and him dressed like a university scholar! Every time the bell jangled, taking the boy away from his eavesdropping, he was impatient with the customers. The minute he got rid of them he returned to his post. He saw that his master, a jovial and talkative man, was no longer silent and in awe of the mad one. He was telling the professor, as if he were a new apprentice, how the cutting block was cleaned, the thin-bladed knives sharpened, and the thrusting spear used. The professor wrote it all down on the tablet. His hand moved back and forth across the white folio with trembling speed, and then he shook sand on the black words.

It was finished at last, for the professor was replacing his belongings in the satchel. He paid the butcher and passed swiftly with great strides through the shop. "Give the meat to the poor," he said, opening the door. The bell jangled and finally its sound and that of his heavy footsteps died away.

The boy faced his master. "Did he tell you what he was up to, or is he too mad?"

"Oh, he's mad enough, but it's not a madness of the rolling eye or the twitching, treacherous hand. It's more a madness of the mind. It's a naughty business he is about He makes a translation of the Bible into German! He wishes to get the passages about the sacrifices right, whatever they be! For a man to change the Word of God"— the master was shouting now—"which is writ, as every fool knows, in the holy Latin, is a blasphemy!"

"Is he from these parts?" The boy's tone was apprehensive.

"I know not, but when he made order for the sheep it was a good German name he gave. Seems I have heard it used in tavern talk, but the why and wherefore of the matter escapes me." He stroked his mustache thoughtfully. "Have you ever heard of one Martin Luther?"

There were other scenes no less fabulous as Luther worked on his translation of the Bible. In order that the gems of the book of *Revelation* might sparkle in the German tongue, Luther borrowed specimens of the court jewels. Consulting Jewish scholars he made studies of the values of the old coins, weights, and measures mentioned in the Old Testament and went then to the market places to find the right German equivalent. He recalled the crude words of loneliness and need and sin the people had poured out to him in the confessional when he had been a priest. He played with children in the street and listened to the talk of men behind the plow. He wanted his translation to "sing the Lord's song in a strange land." He knew that the concepts and thought of the Hebrews and the Greeks would be lost to the people of the byways and the streets of Germany if they were written in the high-sounding German of the universities.

These colorful events took place years after Luther had been excommunicated from the church and threatened with death for his beliefs. Luther lived at the time of transition from the medieval to the modern era. The revival of classical art and learning, the Renaissance, was spreading over western Europe. In Germany, Johann Gutenberg gave impetus to the spread of classical knowledge through printed books. The first book that Gutenberg ran through his press was Jerome's Latin Bible, the Vulgate.

There was a revival in religion, too, the Reformation. Luther led the movement, protesting "the right of the common man to know the Bible and to be saved by his belief in God through the saving grace of Jesus Christ."

It was from the hosts of "protesting groups" who followed Luther's teachings that the name and faith "Protestant" were born.

When the authorities of the church in Rome and in Germany screamed heresy, Luther was put on trial before the emperor, Charles V, in Worms and excommunicated from the church. In his final words of defense he cried out, "I am bound by the Holy Scriptures. My conscience is captive to the Word of God. Unless I am convinced by Scripture or by clear argument, I cannot and will not recant!"

Luther was never convinced that his theories were wrong, and he did not recant. Because his life was threatened, he went into hiding at Wartburg Castle in 1521 and began translating the New Testament from the Greek into German. In the lonely castle, without copyists or assistance of any kind, in the time of flickering lamps and quill pens, he completed the entire work. The first edition of his New Testament was printed in September, 1522.

Luther so stirred the German people with his "Das Newe Testament Deutzsch" and his denunciation of "candles, bells, pictures, masses, cowl, cap, shaven poll, and the whole swarm and rabble of the pope's government" that great confusion broke out among his followers. Destruction of property and abandonment of morals swept the country.

Taking his life in his own hands, Luther returned to Wittenberg, the storm center of the trouble. Here for eight days he preached that the power of the new faith was to build up, not to tear down. He reminded the people that he himself had "opposed indulgences and all the papists, but not with force." He introduced a form of service for the new church with German instead of Latin Bible reading. He released hymns he had written in order to give the people a part in the worship. Two of the best known of these are "A Mighty Fortress Is Our God" and "Away in a Manger."

Luther had no sooner returned to the safety of Wartburg Castle than war broke out between the peasants and the noblemen. Feeling that he was needed in the world, he took the chance of again returning to Wittenberg. Protected by the princes and scholars of Wittenberg who believed in him, he set about building and strengthening the new church. He resumed his teaching at the University and surprised all his friends and foes by marrying. He began then the translation of the Old Testament that took him, as we have described, to butcher shops and court jewelers. It was a task that even for so versatile a man took eleven years. Not until 1534 was his whole translation of the Bible issued.

Speaking of his work to a group of his colleagues and students whom he organized into a Bible Club, Luther betrayed a wonderful sense of humor. "I am now at work translating the Prophets. Good Heavens! How hard it is to make the Hebrew writers speak German. They resist our efforts. They don't want to give up their native tongue for a barbarous idiom, just as the nightingale would not want to change her sweet song to imitate the monotonous cuckoo." Of the translating of *Job*, Luther wrote, "Job insists upon sitting in sackcloth and ashes all the time."

The Bible Club met weekly and brought words they had been chasing all over Germany, personally and by correspondence. These were thoroughly discussed and each member was consulted on points in his specialized field—history, philology, theology, anatomy, physiology. So carefully was the work done that Luther wrote, "Sometimes we could barely translate three lines in four days."

The Bible that was gathered from the language of the butcher and the baker, the children and the plowmen, the scholars and the merchants became the textbook of the modern German language. It opened a new day of literacy and was the unifying source of the national language.

The Bible first sold in Germany for what would approximate three hundred dollars a copy. The people sought it in such numbers, however, that printers hurried to put out more and more editions. Gradually its price was so reduced that even the very poor could afford to buy it. This Bible was the cornerstone of the new Protestant faith. Its reception spurred an Englishman, William Tyndale, to do for his country, his people, and his God what Luther had done for his.

3

The Book Men Died For

THEY had been arguing hotly for an hour. Even Sir John Walsh, at whose table they sat, was becoming uneasy. Young William Tyndale, who was Sir John's household chaplain as well as his children's tutor, was exposing too clearly the spiritual ignorance of the other guests. They were a group of prelates and doctors of theology who could lecture brilliantly for as long as two hours on the physical characteristics of the angels who danced on the point of a pin, of how many angels there were, and the intricacies of the steps they took. But not one of these men, Tyndale demonstrated, knew the Lord's Prayer or even where it was to be found in the Bible. What was more, Tyndale was the only one who thought it mattered. The argument was whether or not a priest of God should know anything of God's Word.

The servants had cleared away the meal, the evening candles had been lighted in the great dining hall, but still the altercation went on. Finally, pounding the boards of the table, one of the distinguished doctors cried, "We would be better off without God's law than without the pope's!"

At this Tyndale shouted, "I defy the pope and all his laws! If God spare my life, ere many years I will cause a boy that driveth the plow to know more of the Scripture than thou doest."

After his guests had gone, Lady Walsh wrung her hands. Because she liked William Tyndale, she rebuked him gently, asking if he did not think he had gone too far. "Oh, Master Tyndale, you are so much talked of now in the alehouses—the preaching place of those blind and rude priests—they already affirm your sayings are heresy, adding moreover unto your sayings, of their own heads, more than ever you spake."

Tyndale offered then to leave the Walsh home, for the embarrassment of the family was clear. They were a courageous couple, however. Their conversion to Tyndale's Lutheran point of view concerning the "simplicity of true faith through Christian living and Bible reading" was sincere. By no means would they allow him to go. In order to save further embarrassment to themselves and Tyndale,

Sir John ceased to invite the prelates to his home. That only made the matter worse.

The Walsh manor was one of the most attractive spots in the lives of the churchmen of the diocese of Gloucestershire. Sir John was a man of considerable wealth, and the hospitality he extended, the best to be had. The resentment of the prelates toward Tyndale was without limit. He, the churchmen complained, was the cause of cutting them off from a comfortable bed and well laden board at the manor.

They lost no time in reporting Tyndale's remarks to Chancellor Parker, supervisor of all priests within the Gloucestershire diocese. The chancellor speedily sent for Tyndale and also called in a few of the irate prelates. They apparently did all the talking, and Tyndale was given no chance to defend himself. Of that session with the chancellor, Tyndale wrote, "He threatened me grievously and reviled me and rated me as though I were a dog."

This interview led Tyndale to decide to move out of the Walsh manor and the diocese. He had no desire to bring harm to the family who had so kindly sheltered him and at the same time enabled and encouraged him to work on his Bible translation, which was against the law. The laws enacted to suppress the Wycliffe version of the Bible were still in effect. Permission to translate the Bible into English could be granted only under very special circumstances by Bishop Tunstall of London. He was in no mood to give a suspected priest like Tyndale any such license.

Tyndale himself was no unlearned man. He had spent

nearly twenty years at the Universities of Oxford and Cambridge, learning and instructing and earning the degree of Master. Now he decided to go to London and, through Bishop Tunstall, seek a living that would enable him to continue his secret translation. But Bishop Tunstall soon showed he had no intention of helping the "young near-heretic" in any way.

Tyndale wearily found a place to preach at St. Dunstan's-in-the-West, London. It was a poor situation. He could hardly make ends meet and had no time for his secret work. His vigorous preaching, however, attracted several men of influence, notably Sir Humphrey Monmouth, a cloth merchant, who took the trouble on several occasions to travel the entire length of London to hear him preach.

Sir Humphrey lent Tyndale money and invited him to his home, where he lived for half a year. For these kindnesses, Monmouth several years later had to defend himself before Cardinal Wolsey. The record of Sir Humphrey's reply to the cardinal contains this information about Tyndale's work habits while secretly translating the New Testament in London: "I took him into my house half a year, and there he lived like a good priest as methought. He studied most part of the day and of the night at his book; and he would eat but sodden meat by his good will and drink but small single beer."

Of his next move Tyndale wrote, "And so in London I abode almost a year; and marked the course of the world; and heard our praters, I would say, our preachers, how they boasted themselves and their high authority; and beheld the pomp of our prelates; and understood at last not only that there was no room in my Lord of London's palace to translate the New Testament, but also that there was no place to do it in all England, as experience doth now openly declare."

After getting a loan of ten pounds from Sir Humphrey, Tyndale said good-by to England, not dreaming that he would never return. In 1524 he landed in Hamburg, Germany.

By the end of a year's exile Tyndale was ready to have his New Testament printed. The English dialects that Wycliffe had stirred together were now taking form as the national language. It was Tyndale's "Newe Testament in simplest language, and in the vulgar tongue" that provided much of the vigor and beauty that began then to characterize the English idiom of that day. Unlike Wycliffe, he had done the whole work himself. Now, however, he went to Cologne, for Hamburg had no printing press, and there employed two printers.

The whole job was to be done under cover. If the news of the printing leaked out, it was feared that England would find some way of suppressing or seizing the work. All went well and soon three thousand copies of the first twenty-two chapters of the book of *Matthew* were stacked in sheets in the workshop.

About that time one of the workmen, over a pot of beer in a tavern, entered into a religious dispute about Luther. Looking very knowing, he drunkenly declared to the whole company, "I could tell plenty about Luther, and he isn't the only one. I could give the names of Englishmen who are planning to make all England Luther-minded."

The dangerous words traveled far. Enemies of Luther picked up the message and took it to John Cochloeus, a man whose anti-Protestant atrocities—committed in the name of loyalty to the pope and God—make him sound more like a Communist spy than a sixteenth-century priest. He made it his personal business to become acquainted with the workmen in the suspected print shop and invited them to his home and the contents of his wine cellar. They talked as freely as the wine flowed. "English merchants are paying for it. They're going to smuggle the Bibles out of Germany in bales of cloth and sell 'em in England."

Cochloeus lost not a moment. He got the city fathers of Cologne to stop the project. He wrote the King of England, Cardinal Wolsey, and Bishop Tunstall and warned them to have all incoming merchant ships searched for the books. But Tyndale lost no time either after a repentant workman confessed the betrayal. Tyndale managed to escape from the print shop with the completed pages before Cochloeus' agents arrived, departing secretly for Worms where he hired another printer. Without mishap or discovery the printing of the New Testament was finished.

The searching of the ships suggested by Cochloeus had been fruitlessly carried out during the winter of 1525. By the time the books made their first appearance in the spring of 1526, the ships were no longer under suspicion. At least six thousand New Testaments invaded England and were distributed throughout the land before anyone in authority knew of their arrival.

When the books were discovered, Bishop Tunstall got

the king to order them to be rooted out and burned. Homes were searched, and not only were the Testaments seized but those who possessed them were arrested as heretics. All Bible owners discovered were also declared heretics and were required to take part in an infamous show staged by Bishop Tunstall and Cardinal Wolsey at Paul's Cross in London. One hundred and fifty-eight baskets of Tyndale's Testaments were piled in the public square, and heretics were forced to throw burning fagots on the books.

The wild flames of that fire lit the faces of the humiliated heretics and the shameless row of bishops who sat watching, but they also lit the curiosity of the crowd gathered to see this free spectacle. The question of the hour was, "Have you seen this naughty translation? Do you know where a man can get a copy of it?"

The merchants, knowing the value of such publicity, smuggled more and more copies into the barrels and bales that entered England and Scotland that year. Several Dutch printers put out additional editions to meet the demand. Although the English authorities tried to buy up or seize as many copies as they could, thousands slipped by hidden in flax and wheat. The public was so eager to see this contraband book they paid well for it, and the merchants were lured to take risks for the high profits involved.

So great was the consternation of the bishop and the cardinal that they imprisoned all they could find who were known to have been friends of Tyndale. Even such an influential man as Sir Humphrey Monmouth was not spared. Excommunication of hundreds, imprisonment of scores, and the burning of several at the stake went on. Agents were employed by the cardinal and instructed to go to Germany, catch Tyndale, and bring him back alive.

Tyndale found refuge with a friend of the Reformation, Philip the Magnanimous of Germany, and resided at Marburg. There, shutting out all thought of personal danger, he turned his attention to the deeper study of Hebrew. He had in mind now the translation of the Old Testament.

Bishop Tunstall went to Antwerp but failing to find trace of Tyndale did what he considered the next best thing. He persuaded a merchant to sell him all the copies of the New Testament he could find, offering a handsome profit. The merchant's name was Augustine Packington, a shrewd man but no friend of Tyndale's foe. The story of that transaction, as Halle, the historian, relates it, is delightful to all who enjoy seeing the wily villain outwitted by the virtuous man.

He [Packington] said to the Bishop, "My lord, if it be your pleasure, I can in this matter do more, I dare say, than most of the merchants of England that are here . . . so that if it be your lordship's pleasure to pay for them . . . I will then assure you to have every book of them that is imprinted and is here unsold. . . ."

"Gentle Mr. Packington, do your diligence and get them; and with all my heart I will pay for them whatsoever they cost you, for the books are erroneous and naught, and I intend surely to destroy them all, and to burn them at Paul's Cross."

Packington went immediately to Tyndale. "William, I know that thou art a poor man and hast a heap of New Testaments and books by thee, for the which thou hast both endangered thy friends and beggared thyself; and I have now gotten thee a merchant."

"Who is the merchant?" said Tyndale.

"The Bishop of London."

"Oh, that is because he will burn them," said Tyndale.

"Yea marry," quoth Packington.

Tyndale was also a quick thinker and saw at once from the expression on Packington's face what he had in mind.

"I am the gladder," said Tyndale, "for these two benefits shall come thereof: I shall get money to bring myself out of debt, and the whole world will cry out against the burning of God's Word; and the overplus of the money shall make me more studious to correct the said New Testament, and so newly to imprint the same once again and I trust the second will much better like you than ever did the first."

And forward went the bargain.

Halle ends the story of how Bishop Tunstall financed the revision of Tyndale's New Testament, by telling that shortly afterward the revised Testament "came thick and three-fold over into England."

Anti-Protestant hatred was sweeping Europe, and agents of the emperor in a surprise move arrested Tyndale and took him to Vilvorde Castle, the state prison of the Low Countries. His trial lasted sixteen months, during which time he finished translating the Old Testament through *Chronicles*. He did this, unsuspected by the authorities, through the aid of his keeper's family, all of whom he had converted. They obtained for him "candles for the evening, paper, Hebrew Bible, Grammar, and

Dictionary" and said of him, "if he be not a good Christian man, we know not whom to trust."

Fate plays strange tricks. During the time that Tyndale was in prison, Tunstall was executed in the Tower of London for treason, and an English translation of the Bible, made by Miles Coverdale, was freely granted to the people. Half-hearted attempts were made in England to get Tyndale returned to his native land, but to no avail. It was the last time a reviser of the Bible would be burned, but not the last time for the burning of a revision. Tyndale was strangled publicly on October 6, 1536, and his body burned. He is reported to have prayed just before he died, "Lord, open the King of England's eyes."

Henry VIII had abolished papal authority in England and had been made sovereign head of the state church. Because the early Church of England preserved many of the Roman Catholic practices, not all of the reformists were pleased. Those who were satisfied came to be called Anglicans and those who dissented, Puritans.

By the time that James I ascended the throne in 1603 there was great dissension among the Anglicans and Puritans, particularly about which of the then current versions of the Bible was official. There was the Bishop's Bible, which the Anglicans preferred, but which the Puritans howled was "popish." The Geneva Bible, which the Puritans used, was declared by the Anglicans "Calvinistic." Shortly after his coronation, King James called together some members of both factions for a discussion of "things amiss in the church." He learned from the conference that there was not only a confusion of Bibles but also a considerable contempt on the part of some of the Puritans for their king's authority.

James then appointed a committee of fifty-four of the best scholars of the land, Anglican and Puritan, commissioned them to prepare a revision, and declared that it would become the official Bible of the Church of England. So zealous was this committee that they made instead a translation of the Bible from the original Greek and Hebrew into seventeenth-century English.

Forty-seven of the fifty-four scholars set to work—what happened to the others is not known—"every particular man of each company to take the same chapter or chapters; and have translated or amended them severally by himself where he thinketh good, all to meet together, confer what they have done, and agree for their parts what shall stand. As any one company hath dispatched any one book in this manner, they shall send it to the rest to be considered of seriously and judiciously. . . ."

The translation was done by three groups in Cambridge, Oxford, and Westminster, and when it was completed, two scholars from each group were elected and sent to London. These final six saw the Bible through the press in 1611, exactly three and one-half years after the project had been started. In this translation in large measure was retained the vigorous wording of Tyndale and Coverdale. Its dedication page reads. "To the Most High and Mightie Prince, James by the Grace of God, King of Great Britaine, France and Ireland, Defender of the Faithe." We know this Bible today as the King James Version, which has led some people from that day to this to give the king credit for having written it at God's command. It has been a popular best-seller among the world's books ever since its publication in the middle of the seventeenth century.

This Bible has been called by the world's thinkers "a masterpiece," "a monument in words," "a noble inheritance and national treasure." The beauty and simplicity of its every line have inspired more poetry, art, and music than any other work of man. The rhythm and cadence of its words have influenced the style of writers from Milton to Thomas Mann, and the oratory of statesmen from Lincoln to Churchill. No one today reading the works of Shelley, Tennyson, Browning, Scott, Macaulay, Hawthorne, Irving, Thoreau, and many others can fully understand their themes, style, and allusions unless he knows something of this Bible. The works of all these writers were colored and enriched because they were brought up in daily contact with the King James Version.

But great and wonderful as the translation was, it was attacked as "modernistic" and the scholars were accused of "perverting the meaning of the Scriptures." It did not achieve for King James the harmony he wanted, for it took fifty years for the people to accept it. Certain of the Puritans, who were called "Separatists," had no intention that their king should put himself on the level with God. They fought him tenaciously on the right to worship when and where they pleased and declared they could obey only such of his laws as did not conflict with their idea of God's laws. King James tried to force the Separatists to accept his belief in the Divine Right of Kings by having them persecuted and imprisoned. Finally, sick of the whole business, he said, "I will make them conform, or I will harry them out of the land."

They chose not to conform. A group of them escaped into Holland and remained there until the day came in 1620 when "the wind being faire, they went aborde ye ship at DelfesHaven . . . where truly dolfull was ye sight of that sade and mournfull parting. . . . Their Revd, pastor falling doune on his knees . . . committed them with most fervent praiers to the Lord and his blessing. And then with mutuall imbrases and many tears, they took their leaves one of another, which proved to be ye last leave to many of them."

One of the most important pieces of cargo on the overloaded *Mayflower* was the Bible, probably the Geneva Bible since the Puritans were among those who for decades spurned the King James Version. In the cabin of the ship the Pilgrim Fathers drew up a compact that began, "In the name of God, Amen. . . . Having undertaken for the glory of God and advancement of the Christian Faith . . . a voyage. . . ." Until they had a constitution, they agreed to live by the tenets of their Bible.

They were the first to flee from religious persecution to the new continent, but they were followed by hosts of others: Moravians, Huguenots, Pietists, Quakers, Jews, Mennonites, Roman Catholics, Presbyterians, Wesleyans. These were a few of the many peoples who had discovered a new freedom in the Bibles that began to appear in all the languages of Europe. The freedom to worship God according to the dictates of their conscience was the cornerstone on which they built their lives in the new land.

People of a Strange Speech

IT was October 28, 1646 when John Eliot, a minister of Roxbury, accompanied by three other Englishmen, journeyed on horseback to Nonantum to preach in the Great Wigwam of Waban, chief of the Massachusetts Indians of that neighborhood. An odd assortment of Indians had gathered there. Some of them had cut their hair and wore hats in ludicrous imitation of the Puritans. Some of them wore their hair long and had their bodies ceremonially painted in bright colors. To these Indians

40

John Eliot earnestly "preached in their own tongue for full two hours."

So great was their amazement at the Englishman speaking their language and so astounding the message of a Father God "in Massachusetts, at Coneetacut, at Quimipeiock, in old England, in this Wigwam, in the next everywhere" that even the modest John Eliot naïvely recorded that "none of them slept Sermon or derided God's messenger." At the close of his talk, hearing the Indians muttering to one another, John Eliot said, "We desire you to propound some questions."

A grave Indian with eyes like an old eagle rose and asked defiantly, "What good does it do for an Indian to pray? Is not the English Book of God proof that Jesus Christ does not understand Indian?"

And what John Eliot answered went something like this: "If it is possible for me, a poor servant of God, in several years to have learned to hear your words with some understanding, can you not believe that God, to whom all things are possible, may hear your every word and know your inmost thoughts with understanding? As for the Book of God, it belongs to every man. Even as you are without it, so once were the people of England. But, be assured, we are even now laboring in order that the words of God may be seen and heard in your tongue."

When John Eliot had arrived in Boston Harbor in 1631, fifteen years before that first sermon in the Massachusetts dialect, he had then no intention of becoming a missionary to the Indians. But the memory of John Robinson's rebuke to the *Mayflower* Pilgrims, "concerning ye killing of those poor Indians. Oh! how happy a thing had it been, if you had converted some . . ." had led him to devote more and more of his time to their conversion.

How to convert them when neither he nor anyone else could converse with them beyond the simplest salutations was the question. There were no books and no writing of any kind in their language. There was no written alphabet. The throaty grunts and guttural noises were barbarous sounds compared with the accent of the Puritan English. The Indian way of life, consisting of a round of war-making, hunting, fishing, idleness, and sleep, was so far removed from the Pilgrim's "work and worship" that even if the bridge of language were gulfed, the gap between the two different cultures would still present impossibilities.

These things John Eliot pondered, pacing the rude paths between his garrisoned home and church. He knew his home and church would have to be barricaded for safety against the hostile Indians until the key to their language was discovered and the Indians drawn into the community by understanding. The alternative was one he abhorred—the killing of more and more Indians until there were no longer enough of them left to be a threat. But he had no key to the Massachusetts dialect. All he had was the wild sound of the words; the meaning was locked in that sound.

By great good fortune one day he learned from a traveler about an Indian called Job Nesutan, over whom there was much rejoicing in Dorchester because he was about to join the church. He was an Indian warrior who had been taken captive, the traveler casually told John Eliot, in the

Pequot Wars. Serving in the "house of one Mr. Richard Caliott of Dorchester," he had learned English so well and rapidly that he was the "amazement of all who entered that household."

Here was a key, an Indian who could speak English. John Eliot had learned from his Greek and Hebrew studies at Cambridge, England, that aptitude in one language often means skill in others. Would this Long Island Indian know the dialect of the Massachusetts Indians? Eliot mounted his horse and headed for Dorchester.

Inside of two weeks Job Nesutan was a member of the Eliot household. Yes, indeed, he spoke the Massachusetts dialect and "with an exceeding clear pronouncement." Writing of Job in a letter to England, Eliot said, "This Indian is ingenious, can read; and I taught him to write, which he quickly learnt. . . ."

They sat together by sunlight and by candlelight, whenever John Eliot could spare the time from his teaching and preaching in the church of Roxbury. Job taught Eliot Indian words, which he learned with difficulty to say, to spell out, and, finally, to put down on paper. By studying sentences, by following every noun and verb down a hundred different trails, by asking Job a hundred times, "Can this word be used here?" Eliot was able to analyze the basic structure of the language. From that analysis he constructed rules and so built his famous *Indian Grammar*.

But no amount of academic study can give a person facility in speaking a language. John Eliot went out, as Luther had once walked the streets of Wittenberg, to the Indians within the bounds of Roxbury. Sitting around their fires in the middle of their wigwams, he learned their customs and beliefs. He discovered that, however wild and undeveloped it might be, religious sentiment was there. He wrote often to England pleading for help for his work among the Indians, telling that they were not all rude savages, that they recognized the divine power in natural things, that they spoke familiarly and reverently of "the sun god and the moon god and the spirits that moved in the winds and waters." They had, too, he discovered, a kind of priesthood—men and women called "powwows" whose business it was to cure diseases and to preserve crops by means of herbal brews and magical incantations.

After the tasks of compiling thousands of words of the language, of writing the grammar, of mastering the speaking idiom so that he could think, preach, and pray in their tongue, he was ready to begin the task of translating the Bible. His job was a hundred times more difficult than the work of previous translators mentioned. For centuries before Wycliffe, Tyndale, and Luther, England and Germany had had thousands of travelers and merchants who came to the cities introducing, with their wares, new ideas and thoughts. In Massachusetts, the Indians had had only two decades of contact with the English settlers, and that, because of the language barrier and elements of invasion in their arrival, was hardly an enriching contact.

How was Eliot to convey the Oriental concepts in the Hebrew and Greek Scriptures to the children of the wigwam and the forest? To men who knew the deer of the woods, how was the desert camel to be explained? How were men who were beardless to understand the reference to the beard of Aaron?

Eliot began with the Lord's Prayer and the Ten Commandments—which sounds simple enough, but it wasn't. "Our Father which art in heaven" alone took hours of exploring discussion. The Indian word for "father," indeed the relationship of father, conveyed nothing of the meaning it had in the Hebrew sense or in the English culture. But the Indian, Eliot discovered, did have a word that had the meaning of "loving care for his children" and "headship" and that word was "chief." "Great Spirit" meant "head of a host of lesser spirits" and so smacked of heathenism to John Eliot.

And the word "heaven" offered problems. There were in the language of the Massachusetts Indians words for "blue sky" and "white sky" and "evening sky" and "morning sky," but no concept for "heaven." Eliot talked with the Indians about it at length and learned at last that the dwelling place of the "Great Spirit" was in the "regions of the far west part of the skies." It was not a geographic location, a fixed point; it was beyond the traveling powers of any living Indian, however fleet his foot or full-blooded his horse—it was, in fact, "heaven."

Eliot had to borrow Anglo-Saxon words for concepts like "God," "temple," "Pharisee," and "rabbi," even as Tyndale had borrowed the latter two from the Hebrew.

The word hunt and the making of new words went on. Eliot gave the meaning of "duke" to *"mugwump"* (a word that has entered our language), which he used in translating *Genesis* 36:30, making the verse read: "*Mugwump Dishon, Mugwump Ezer, Mugwump Dishan. . . .*" The substitution of foreign words and the explaining of them continued for as much of each day as Eliot could spare for twenty years. Finally the whole Bible was translated, printed, and put into the hands of the Indians of the Massachusetts Bay Colony.

The New Testament had been finished by 1658 but did not appear in print until 1661. A new press, type, and a printer were sent over from England to Cambridge, Massachusetts, by "The Corporation for the Promoting and Propagating of the Gospel among the Indians of New England," an institution that the work of John Eliot had been instrumental in starting.

But the printer, Johnson, whom the corporation had sent, was a divorced man and caused many doubts among the Puritans. He was often stopped from working for as much as six months at a time. These periods of unemployment he devoted to drunken sprees while the church fathers argued and prayed over the ethics of allowing an English heathen to prepare the gospel for the Indian heathen. Nor were those all the problems that beset the printing.

An Indian called James Printer, who had been educated at "the charity school in Cambridge," was employed because of his ability to read English and his native language. His interest in printing had led to his being named "Printer." He gave Johnson assistance in proofreading the Indian text, but in the middle of the job he became angry with the English and ran away to help the Indians fight them.

Then the funds ran out, and Eliot had to make repeated appeals to England for further help. It seems miraculous that with all these adversities the printing of the New Testament took only three years. When we consider that it sometimes took ships, which carried the letters back and forth, as long as seven weeks to cross the Atlantic, this achievement was marvelous.

By the time the Bible was ready, a generation of the children of Christian Indians had learned to read and write the Massachusetts dialect, principally in the schools set up by John Eliot in the Indian town of Natick. Some Indians were, at the time of the Bible's publication, studying for the ministry at Harvard College, but they were so few as still to be a great novelty.

In Dedham, Roxbury, Dorchester, and many other communities around Boston Harbor, Indians friendly to the English were called "Praying Indians" to differentiate them from those outside the community bounds who were not Christianized and who continued to attack the white settlers.

Eliot's Indian Bible has become one of the rare books in the collectors' world, the novelty and delight of linguists and philologists. It was the first book printed in an American Indian language and the first Bible published in the Western Hemisphere. How good a translation it was no one can guess, for today there is no man living who speaks the language of the Massachusetts Indian. Within fifty years of his death, the tribe of Indians for whom John Eliot labored so long became extinct.

There are a few copies of this famous Bible in existence. Every once in a while some New England attic yields another. As late as 1840 a mutilated copy, being used as waste paper, was discovered in a Dorchester barber shop.

A copy of the New Testament is in the library of Harvard University. The copy of the entire Bible sent to Charles II is in the British Museum, and copies of the first and second editions are owned by the American Bible Society. Several other copies are priceless items in American and British private collections. The pages of line-long, hard-looking words read like the Jabberwocky passages of Lewis Carroll's *Through the Looking Glass.*

It was so far from Eliot's purpose, however, to produce a rare item of Americana that it might be supposed that he failed in his missionary aim. In the sense that he would have understood it, he did. Neither he nor any of the Puritans dreamed that the Massachusetts Indians would be so cruelly wiped out. But in the sense that he was the first of a long line of missionary-translators to compile the words and study the character of an unwritten language to produce a whole Bible, he was successful, a brilliant pioneer. Linguists, scholars, and missionary-translators of today have built their techniques on the pattern of Eliot's research, word hunting, and grammar building. Because of his example, the languages of hundreds of primitive peoples, who knew only oral communication, have been reduced to writing in order that they, too, might have the Bible.

Joseph Renville sat tailor-fashion on a chair before the roaring fireplace that defied the twenty-below-zero weather outside. On packing cases in front of the candle-lit counting table, ready with pen and ink, paper, and open books, sat the three missionaries, Dr. Thomas S.

Williamson, Mr. Gideon H. Pond, and the Reverend Stephen R. Riggs. On the bench around the walls of the room sat Running-Walker, Left Hand, Reaches-to-the-Tail, Thunder-Face, Eagle-Help, and other Dakota men of the village. They smoked and listened, with eyes half closed, as Dr. Williamson read from the French Bible, *"Car Dieu a tant aimé le monde, qu'il a donné son seul Fils . . ."*

Stephen Riggs waited with his pen poised above the white paper, while Renville removed his pipe and spat thoughtfully into the hearth. *"Wakantanka Cinbintku kin Wicoicagne en u si kin . . ."*

"Wait a minute, please, Joseph," Riggs begged. Renville threw back his head and laughed. Although he was the best of friends with the missionaries and a willing helper in their every task, he was not above enjoying a sense of superiority over them. It delighted him that he —a half-breed fur trader, barely able to read and write —could hold these scholars at his mercy because of his knowledge of spoken French, Dakota, and English.

"'For God so loved the world . . .' I've got that far, Joseph," said Riggs apologetically.

And Renville, his eyes twinkling, patiently and slowly gave the Dakota words for the French, going over and over some of them as many as six times until Riggs had them all down. When the verse was complete, Riggs read it back to the Indians, who nodded if they understood or who discussed it if the meaning was not clear. Riggs laid down his pen, and Pond picked it up. Thus they alternated through verse after verse, so that writer's cramp would not halt the work.

49

Outside, the wind howled and flung the snow against the stockade palings. They were in the third winter of translating and had completed only the Gospel of *Mark* and part of *John*. Stephen Riggs was tired. There was a nagging persistence in his mind that a better and a truer way to do this task would be to master the language himself. If only he could translate into Dakota, not from Renville's dubious French, but from the original Greek and Hebrew.

Three winters—three years. The bleak winds outside said it was longer. It seemed longer since he and Mary had left Ipswich, Massachusetts, that first day of March in 1837. They had traveled day and night by stage to New York City, to Philadelphia, and across the mountains to Pittsburgh, sailing down the Ohio River by steamer to the Mississippi, reaching St. Louis on May 8. He smiled, remembering that the boat for Fort Snelling had left on Sunday morning. They had not boarded it because Mary would not violate the Sabbath or allow the men who would have had to load their furniture to violate it. But that faithful adherence to God's command had not cost them a moment. They had left on Monday by ox cart for Galena, Illinois, and there caught the selfsame steamer. Journeying two full weeks up the Mississippi, they passed beyond the last cabins of the pioneers. They saw then the first of the tepees and villages of the land of the Dakota Indians.

It was on June 1, a beautiful day, Riggs recalled, that they had arrived at Fort Snelling, the home of the first mission among the Dakotas. They had remained at the Fort several months, getting acquainted with the white men and women there, all of whom belonged either to the military or the mission.

Mary and he had then left Fort Snelling and journeyed by barge, manned by four men at the oars and one at the stern. It took thirteen days to reach the "place of the speaking lake," Lac-qui-parle, which was to be their home. He remembered his first meeting with Dr. Williamson, an Ohio physician. Williamson had established a medical mission two years before at Lac-qui-parle and had won the friendship of the most influential man for miles about, the fur trader, Joseph Renville.

Riggs pushed aside his memories and picked up his pen again. He noted that Joseph was being very patient tonight. The verse that Pond had just taken was very difficult. Eagle-Help had been querulous about it, but he had a keen mind, keener than all the rest.

And so they worked, until fatigue and the smell of the smoke of the fire, the pipes, and the candles and the fur skins curing in the storeroom beyond, made them sleepy. Then they filed out of the stockade, Joseph coming out to put up the heavy bar on the door behind them. They pushed through the snow, Running-Walker leading, the others following in single file, the Indians going to their tepees and the white men to their hewn-log house. Riggs once described that house in a letter to "the States," for at that time Lac-qui-parle was part of the Northwest Territory. He wrote:

"Dr. Williamson had erected a log house a story and a half high. In the lower part was his own living room and also a room with a large open fireplace, which, then and for several years afterward, was used for the school and Sabbath assemblies. In the upper part there were three rooms, still in an unfinished state. The largest of these, ten feet wide and eighteen feet long, was appropriated to our use. We fixed it up with loose boards overhead and quilts nailed up to the rafters, and improvised a bedstead, as we had been unable to bring ours farther than Fort Snelling.

"That room we made our home for five winters. There were some hardships about such close quarters, but, all in all, Mary and I never enjoyed any five winters more than those we spent in that upper room. There our first three children were born. There we worked in acquiring the language. There we received our Dakota visitors. There I wrote and wrote again my ever growing dictionary. And then, with what help I could obtain I prepared for the printer the greater part of the New Testament in the language of the Dakotas. It was a consecrated room."

It has been said of Stephen Riggs that he "made the Dakota language," but this he denied. "It was not part of our business to make the Dakota language. It was simply the missionary's work to report it faithfully and, of course, to be as nearly phonetic as possible. The English alphabet was to be used as far as it could be. These were the principles that guided and controlled the writing of Dakota."

But say what he would, it was Riggs who determined how to express "four *clicks,* two *gutturals,* and a *nasal*" that were outside the realm of English phonetics. This he accomplished by use of marked letters and the introduction of "q," "c," and "j," letters not needed as they are in English.

It was Riggs who compiled the Dakota dictionary, which contains more than ten thousand words and which he describes as "incidental to our missionary work." With funds for printing contributed by the Historical Society of Minnesota and the American Board of Commissioners for Foreign Missions, this dictionary was offered to the Smithsonian Institution and brought out as one of their series of contributions to knowledge. During the course of printing in New York City the printing office burned and many pages of the manuscript perished—which Riggs also tossed off as an "ordinary incident."

Eagle-Help was largely responsible for Riggs's mastery of Dakota. Like Job Nesutan he had natural linguistic aptitudes and was the first Dakotan to learn to read and write his language, but for many years he was only a "part-time Christian." Every few months the spirit world would tell him to make *Joomene wachepe,* which meant that he would summon about twenty young Indians who painted themselves, fasted, feasted, and drilled by dancing the "no flight" dance and then went off to make war on the Ojibwa Indians. Gradually, however, Eagle-Help ceased going on the warpath, but his reason caused Riggs to wonder if it was "in accord with living a true Christian life." Eagle-Help declared that his knowledge of letters, particularly the Bible, had interfered with his communications from the spirit world.

By the time of the publication of the Bible, between three and four thousand Indians could read their language; quite a section of the Sioux nation had become civilized and Christianized; and there were many Indian churches and scores of native pastors.

How does a man who has worked forty years on a Bible translation feel when the book finally appears? Here is a letter dated March 30, 1880, upon receipt of Riggs's first bound copy: "Yesterday there came to me by mail from the Bible House a most beautiful copy of the Dakota Bible. . . . 'Bless the Lord, oh my soul and all that is within me bless his holy name.' And I feel like adding, Bless the American Bible Society. . . . I look at it and think of the two good right hands that worked for four decades in writing and rewriting those pages, one is mouldering in the dust and the other—sometimes a feeling of numbness creeps over it, admonishing me that its work is almost done, but the work remains. . . . After what I have already said I need hardly ask you to present my most hearty thanks to the Bible Society for giving to our Dakota pastors and churches this magnificent Bible."

5

Island Keepers of the Word

"DEAR SIRS: I have in my possession sent to us by our son, who has been stationed somewhere in the Pacific islands, a Bible that he exchanged with one of the natives for one of his own. Is it permissible for you to tell me what language this Bible is written in? It is published by your organization, having your name on the front page. It has our alphabet. I have discovered the meaning of some of the words by reading in my own Bible and comparing it with this one, a study that is most interesting.

"Our son's description of these natives and their religious services is very, very interesting and impressive. He enjoyed going immensely and marveled at their fine spirit. He loved to hear them sing. He also said they were all Christians and every native went to church every Sunday. I wonder how the Bible got there and if you could tell me where I might find out something about the first missionaries to the Pacific islands.

"Any information you can give by examining the attached quotation will be greatly appreciated, as I would like to know what language this wonderful little Bible is written in."

This letter, written in 1944, was just a little different from many others received by the librarian of the American Bible Society. Many women had written enclosing scraps of native Bibles or quotations from Bibles in strange tongues in an effort to find out where in the Pacific area their sons, husbands, and brothers were located. This woman wanted to know, as well, how the Bible first came to the Pacific islands. Since the quotation she had enclosed was in the language of the Gilbertese, the story of how this book came to the Gilbert Islands is the story of Hiram Bingham, father and son.

Hiram Bingham, who translated the Bible into Gilbertese, was the son of a missionary family who landed in Hawaii in 1820 before he was born. His father and mother, Mr. and Mrs. Hiram Bingham, and twelve other missionaries sailed from Boston on the brig *Thaddeus* on October 23, 1819. After a grim voyage of eighteen thousand miles they cast anchor on April 14, 1820, at Kailua, the principal village of Hawaii and home of the king. Before they could settle anywhere they had to obtain permission of Liholiho, the king of the Islands, ruler of the one hundred and thirty thousand people.

King Liholiho was very dubious but not hostile, when Hiram Bingham asked permission to settle. He answered, through the trader-interpreter, "If I receive and patronize you missionaries, I shall not be allowed but one wife." He grinned affectionately at his five wives, who sat fanning him and holding gourd spit cups for the black juice of the betel he was chewing. Since there was very little Hiram Bingham or any of the missionaries could say to this without first having said many other things, they determined to let their own example speak for them in the matter and to concentrate first on winning the king's permission to settle.

They presented him with a beautiful copy of the English Bible, which he liked very much although he could not read a word of English, Hawaiian, or any other language. "Indeed in the whole land," Hiram Bingham wrote back to Boston, "there was neither book, pen, nor pencil for amusement or business or for acquiring information or communicating thought." The king insisted on English lessons then and there, with which Hiram Bingham obliged. The king was proud as a child when he could say, which he did at the top of his lungs, "How do you do! Aloha!"

The next thing the missionaries did was to invite the king and his royal family aboard ship to dine. When the day of the dinner came, the party came down the beach with servants carrying huge Chinese umbrellas over the royal heads, and *kalilis*, plumed rods of nobility. They got into a double canoe manned by eighteen nearly naked rowers and were conveyed with spirit to the side of the *Thaddeus*.

The king wore a narrow girdle around his waist, a green silk scarf over his shoulders, a string of beads, and a feather wreath, so that without shirt, shoes, stockings, or trousers he met the first white women he had ever seen. His wives were dressed in skirts made of layers of thin unwoven bark cloth and wore wreaths of bright hibiscus flowers on their long black hair. They gazed at the costumes of the missionary women in utmost fascination, peering under their poke bonnets and yanking up their skirts to stare and giggle at their high buttoned boots.

The king was enchanted with the forks and knives, and his intent to steal them was forestalled by the gift of a set. The next day the king returned the invitation, which the missionaries refused because it was the Sabbath. This threw the king into a rage until he was made to understand that party-going on the Sabbath was a "Jehovah taboo."

On Monday, however, the missionary party came ashore and sat, as the Hawaiians did, on mats spread on the ground under the mango trees. The missionaries dutifully dipped their fingers in the dishes of fish and poi and drank water from cocoanut shells but passed up the bowl of dog flesh.

Everybody had such a good time that the king finally decided he liked the missionaries. They could land wherever they wanted, he said, and "stay a year." *One* year? It was a good thing the missionaries didn't stop to worry

58

about that, for as time proved, that year lengthened into decades.

The king, with a royal gesture, provided one of his best huts for the two missionary families who were to remain with him on the island of Hawaii. The gift hut was three and a half feet high, had no floor, windows, or furniture, and was completely verminous. Here Dr. and Mrs. Holman and Mr. and Mrs. Thurston stayed until they built themselves better quarters.

The Binghams then sailed to the island of Oahu and disembarked at Honolulu, at that time a settlement of about four thousand inhabitants. There in grass huts they set up their mission and enclosed it in a fence of slender poles. Sometimes as many as a hundred natives gathered to peer through the fence at them in fascination and to laugh with childlike delight at everything the missionaries did.

"We set ourselves," wrote Hiram Bingham, "to the acquisition of the Hawaiian language, reducing it to written form and preparing books of instruction in it for the nation and teaching all classes to use them as speedily as possible."

Only a month passed before a school for children was opened in Honolulu and "ingenuity and kindness were taxed to give interest enough to the school exercises to induce those who came once to come again, day after day, when the sun should reach a certain elevation pointed out in the heavens."

So great was the success of Bingham's school that the king, hearing of it, objected that children would learn faster than he would. He said he would like to have the school closed. Thurston tactfully pointed out that while the children were learning Hawaiian, the king was learning English, which was much harder. This mollified the king. He applied himself so well that in three months he was able to read portions of his English Bible, which he did with more loud glee than quiet understanding.

Meanwhile, the rest of the missionary party had landed on the island of Kauai. They, too, had been busy teaching English. King Kaumualii of that island wanted to learn it so that he might read the Bible that had been given to him. Of a different caliber from Liholiho, he put his new writing ability to good use in a thank-you letter to the secretary of the American Board. Filling two whole pages with a childlike scrawl, Kaumualii sent the following message to the people who had given him the Bible:

"Dear Friends: I wish to write a few lines to you to thank you for the good book you was so kind as to send. I think it is a good book, one that God gave us to read. I hope all my people will soon read this, and all good books. I believe that my idols are good for nothing, and that your God is the only true God—the one that made all things. My idols I have hove away—they are no good—they fool me—they do me no good. I give them cocoanuts, plantains, hogs, and good many things, and they fool me at last. Now I throw them all away. I have done now. When your good people learn me, I worship your God. I feel glad your good people come here to help us—we know nothing. I thank you for giving my son learning. I thank all America people. Accept this from your friend, King Kaumualii."

Meanwhile Bingham and Thurston were studying the orthography of the Hawaiian language and making an alphabet. They discovered that with twelve letters, a, e, i, o, u, h, k, l, m, n, p, and w, they could express every sound in the pure Hawaiian dialect. They noted that consonants were never doubled and that every word or syllable ended in a vowel. In order not to throw out the consonants of the English alphabet that would be needed in names like David, Boaz, Ruth, Ezra, and others in the translation of the Bible they already were planning, another group of letters was adopted. This group included b, d, f, g, r, s, t, v, and z, and were to be taught only after the Hawaiians had mastered the main alphabet and could read pure native words.

On January 7, 1822, the printing press that Hiram Bingham had asked for arrived. King Liholiho, who had by that time moved to Honolulu and made it the capital of the Islands, came to see the "new engine." The king was allowed to pull the lever down and was delighted to see the clean white sheet of paper covered with the words of his own language, which he had by then learned to read.

The introduction of printing in the language of the people gave new life to the schools and churches, and in a few weeks there were more than five hundred new learners. When the king made a tour of his islands, he took spelling books, instead of ceremonial robes, as gifts to his chiefs.

Hiram Bingham had translated hymns into the language and these were now sung ecstatically by the singing people of Hawaii in the churches, which were built like grass huts. On August 4, 1822, Hiram Bingham recorded that he could dispense with his interpreter and preached his first sermon and "addressed the throne of grace in the language of the country."

The next Sunday King Liholiho and his mother, the highest ranking woman in the Islands, attended Hiram Bingham's church to hear him preach in Hawaiian. They came in an unpainted American-built wagon drawn by men, since the island had no horses nor oxen. The congregation under the plantain trees was a thousand strong. At the close of this service Hiram Bingham performed the first Christian marriage to take place in the Hawaiian Islands. He married Thomas Hopu, who became shortly afterward the first native pastor, to Delia, one of the prize pupils of the first girls' school. The queen mother was so overcome by the solemnity of the whole affair that she wept loudly throughout the service.

A few days later King Liholiho wrote a surprising letter to his rival, the king of the Society Islands. He wrote it in his newly acquired English, although he well knew the king of the Society Islands would have to employ an interpreter to read it. While he might be suspected of wishing to show superiority, it is, nevertheless, an interesting letter.

"O Mahina—I now make a communication to you. I have compassion towards you on account of your son's dying. Love to you and the *alii*, chiefs of your islands. I now serve the God of you and us. We are now learning the *palapala* [Bible]. When I become skilful in learning I will then go and visit you. May you be saved by Jesus Christ."

When King Liholiho's mother was dying, she requested baptism. She sent for her son and said to him, "This is my charge to you. . . . Take care of these lands and the people. Kindly protect the missionaries. Walk the straight path. Observe the Sabbath. Serve God. . . . Obey God's word that you may prosper and meet me in heaven. . . ." To the chiefs she said, "Protect the teachers who have come to this land of dark hearts; give heed to their instruction; reject not the commands of God. . . . He is a good God. Our former gods were vain. . . ."

In November of 1828 the king and the chiefs, who had taken this charge solemnly, proclaimed and caused to be published the first written laws of the land. These were a few scattered rulings against "murder, theft, and adultery," worded in the unmistakable pattern of the Ten Commandments. The same week the first sheet of the translation of Luke's Gospel was printed in Hawaiian in Honolulu. The translation of the Gospels by Matthew, Mark, and John had already been sent to the United States to be printed there.

In the years that followed, large portions of the Old Testament were printed in separate editions and there were several editions of the New Testament. But not until 1839, after nineteen years of preaching, teaching, and healing, could Hiram Bingham write, "The entire translation of the Bible is published!" It was a book that, in the hands of native scholars and preachers, brought thousands more to the churches. It is today considered by linguists remarkable for the few foreign words—like *Sabi* for Sabbath, *Baptizo* for baptize, *Iehova* for Jehovah—that had to be introduced.

Access to the Bible in their own language and a generation of children who had grown up learning to read it gave rise to a people infused with new-born national sentiments. The need for a change in the structure of the government was expressed on all sides. In 1839 a complete written code of laws was adopted and in 1840 a constitution. In other words, statute law now took the place of common law, the first big step in the civilization of any people.

The new young king, grandson of Liholiho, entered upon a long struggle with the British, French, and American governments for the independence of his islands. As part of this campaign, Hiram Bingham visited Washington in 1841, presented to Congress a copy of the Bible in Hawaiian, and addressed the members, giving a brief history of his twenty-one years in the Islands. The young king went to England on a similar errand and had an audience with Queen Victoria.

In 1845 the Legislative Council of Hawaii was assembled in Honolulu for an important proclamation by their king, who told them that the independence of their nation was assured. Part of his historic speech follows:

"The independence of our kingdom has been most explicitly recognized by the United States, Great Britain, France, and Belgium. From each of these powers we have received the most friendly assurances. It is our wish to cultivate the relations of peace and friendship with all nations, and to treat the subjects of all with equal justice. . . .

"We are well aware that the Word of God is the cornerstone of our kingdom. Through its influence we have been introduced into the family of independent nations of the earth. It shall therefore be our constant endeavor to govern our subjects in the fear of the Lord; to temper justice with mercy in the punishment of crime; and to reward industry and virtue. . . ."

That, then, was the ultimate work of the father, Hiram Bingham.

The son, Hiram Bingham, was born in the Hawaiian Islands in 1831. He returned to the United States for his education, and after graduation from Yale he decided to do for the Gilbert Islands what his father and Thurston had done for Hawaii.

His struggles were no less than his father's, perhaps greater. He did not have his father's physical endurance, did much of his translation while ill in bed, and had only the help of his wife and of Moses Kaure, a former pupil. He, too, had to master an unwritten language, build an alphabet, compile words, make a dictionary and grammar before he could turn to translation. It took him forty years, for this work was done in the midst of the thousand and one daily tasks required of a missionary.

It took him five years to translate *Matthew,* and this he sent by the ship *Morning Star* to be printed in Honolulu. For thirteen months he waited with great anticipation for the ship's return with the precious printed book. But when the ship came, the manuscript was returned to him with a printing press and a message, "Couldn't you print it yourself?"

Despairing at the time and energy it would take for

him to set up the press and learn the new trade, of which he knew nothing, and too discouraged and disappointed to sleep, he spent the night in prayer.

In the morning a boatload of bedraggled sailors came ashore and sought his house because they heard he could speak English. They had been shipwrecked a hundred miles offshore and had a hair-raising tale to tell. What must Bingham have felt when one of those sailors, seeing in the house the unassembled press, casually mentioned he used to be a printer. The book of *Matthew* was in the hands of hundreds of Gilbert Islanders within the month!

These were the men, father and son, whose lives of devotion to God gave the Bible in their own language to the Hawaiians and Gilbertese. Without their Christian purpose to share God through his universal Word, the Binghams would never have reduced to written languages tongues that had never before been written down. Without knowledge of written languages there would not have existed the means of communication that enabled many Pacific islanders to shelter and befriend an untold number of American men in their time of terrible need during World War II.

To the Pacific islands, as to England, dedicated Christian men brought, through the Bible, a new revelation of personal and national freedom. Not only did the possession of the Bible in their own tongues make it possible for these people to grow as Christians, but the printed page also opened the door for the whole of human culture to reach them.

6

The Price

of

Splendor

ADONIRAM JUDSON sat on the moonlit veranda with his throbbing head in his hands, reviewing with bitterness the seeming failure of his six years in Rangoon. After all he had done to try to win converts among a disinterested people, now, by order of the viceroy, those few who had responded with an interest in Christ were being threatened and molested.

Just a few months before, he had opened his *zayat* (resthouse), a church and religious schoolroom made of bamboo and thatch, whitewashed to distinguish it from other roadside *zayats*. Day after day he sat before the Christian *zayat* crying in Burmese, "Ho, everyone that thirsteth." To those who stopped, he poured out his heart and gave each of them portions of the book of *Matthew* that he had translated and printed before the government had banished his press. The literate among the Burmans read noisily, listening to him inattentively, often heckling him. Few of them ever stopped more than once.

How had he ever believed his message would have a chance with people who for centuries had worshiped the golden image of Gautama Buddha? Every thought of these people was built on the beautiful but pessimistic writings of the Lord Gautama. They had been taught that life's highest goal was nirvana, the blowing out of all desires of body and soul.

He would go mad if he went on thinking this way. Wearily he lifted his head and picked up his pen to make a long-postponed entry in his journal: "November 1, 1819. We vacated the *zayat,* as we have several days of late, beginning to query whether it is prudent to go boldly on proclaiming a new religion, at the hazard of incensing the government and drawing down such persecution as may deter all who know us from an inquiry."

How could he record that six years here had cost the life of his first child and had been a drain on the health of his frail American wife? How could he put down that all he had to show for this sacrifice were three Burmese converts—men who were so afraid of the new emperor's wrath against all who would not worship Buddha that they had requested secret baptism by night?

Judson now paced up and down the veranda. The thought swelled in his fevered imagination that should his act of baptism be discovered and the three Burmans tortured to death, he, and he alone, would be responsible.

James Coleman, his new assistant of six months, came onto the veranda and said abruptly, "I've been wondering, Judson. Why don't we go to see the new king and ask for religious tolerance? I feel I'm not doing anything here. You, at least, have mastered the language. You can work on your New Testament, but I can't help you. I'll never be able to read or write with those animated blots that pass for an alphabet!"

"Mastered the language?" Judson muttered heavily. "I've been here six years and I've just scratched the surface."

"Well, then," Coleman persisted, "why don't we go to King Bagyidaw himself and find out where we stand or" —he paused—"get out of Burma?"

To go to the king, whose palace was in Ava, three hundred and fifty miles away, was, in 1819, a journey worthy of explorers, but Judson and Coleman started as soon as they could get ready. It took them thirty-five days by inland waters—ten miles a day. From the hilltops of every town and village they passed, by sunlight and by moonlight, the great blind faces of the huge Buddhas glinted down upon them. They came at last to Ava. They reached the alabaster palace gates, ascended stairs of flawless white marble, passed down corridors of ebony, went through doors encrusted with jewels, and entered the throne room. The high dome and giant pillars in this room were completely covered with gold.

While they waited for the king, Judson gave the court minister their petition, one of his tracts, and a beautiful six-volume Bible in English. The Bible was to be presented as a gift to the king.

The king arrived with all the majesty of a great Eastern monarch, and the head of every petitioner touched the floor. Only the missionaries knelt with folded hands. The king seated himself on a cushioned dais and, pointing at Judson and Coleman, questioned his minister, "Who are these?"

Before the minister could open his mouth, Judson replied, "The teachers, great king."

"What! You speak Burmese? Are you teachers of religion?" The king leaned forward, staring at their black suits, which stood out sharply in the midst of the reds and blues and golds of the Burmese *pasos* (skirts). "Why do you dress so?"

He appeared pleased with the answers Judson made and commanded the petition that they had given the minister to be read to him.

The petition said that the American teachers presented themselves to receive the favor of the excellent king, asking that they might preach their religion in these dominions and that those who were pleased with their religion and wished to listen to and be guided by it, whether foreigners or Burmans, might be exempt from government molestation.

Stretching out his hand, the king beckoned for the petition to be brought to him. The minister crawled forward and presented it and the tract. The king read from the tract, "There is one eternal God, beside him there is no God." His face stiffened with anger. He dashed the papers to the floor. The minister picked up the petition and tract and gave them to Judson, indicating that he and Coleman had been dismissed.

Outside the throne room they waited two hours for the minister to advise them what more, if anything, they could do. He came at last and interpreted the royal gesture. "In regard to your petition, His Majesty gives me no orders. In regard to your sacred books, His Majesty has no use for them. Take them away."

Judson and Coleman returned to Rangoon with only one thought in mind, to accept their failure. They began to lay plans for starting a new mission for the Burmese-speaking people of Chittagong, a city under British protection.

But when Judson told his three converts that he was leaving because he had failed in his attempt to win freedom for the new religion, they challenged him with the courage of their faith. "Stay at least," they said, "until a little church of ten is collected and a native teacher is set over it and then, if you must go, we will not say nay. This religion will spread of itself. The king cannot stop it."

Judson stayed.

Within a month there were nine converts in his church. Afraid now to employ a Burman teacher, who might betray him to the government, Judson proceeded to do his translation of the Bible alone. When he had completed the *Epistle to the Ephesians,* his small congregation told him it was much easier to understand than the translation of *Matthew.* This he had done earlier with the help of a renegade Buddhist monk. Encouraged, Judson redoubled his efforts in the language. He soon sent a revised manuscript of *Ephesians* and the first part of *Acts* to Serampore, India, with a request that an edition of six hundred of each be printed.

Of his study of this language, Judson wrote, "When we find the letters and words all totally destitute of the least resemblance to any language we have ever met with, and these words not clearly divided and distinguished, as in Western writing, by breaks and points, and capitals, but run together in one continuous line, a sentence or paragraph seeming to the eye but one long word; when, instead of separate characters on paper, we find only obscure scratches on dried palm leaves strung together and called a book; when we have no dictionary and no interpreter to explain a single word and must get something of the language before we can avail ourselves of the assistance of a native teacher—that is work!"

Because of the fact that the mission was watched closely by the government, Judson's growing success in the language was well known. When Dr. Jonathan Price came to join the Rangoon Mission, the king requested both him and Judson to come to the capital in Ava at government expense. Price was to give the court medical aid and Judson to be an interpreter. Judson had been in the king's presence several days, interpreting everything Price said to the king and everything the king said to Price, before the king spoke directly to him. "And you in black, what are you? A medical man, too?" He knew very well who Judson was.

"Not a medical man, but a teacher of religion, Your Majesty."

"Have any embraced your religion?"

"Not here in Ava," Judson evaded.

"Are there any in Rangoon? Are they foreigners?"

Trembling lest he bring the Rangoon church to ruins, Judson said quietly, "There are some foreigners and some Burmans."

Several days later the king turned to Judson again. "These Burmans who embrace your religion—do they dress like Burmans? How often do they come?"

Wishing to shift the emphasis from his converts to himself, Judson replied, "I preach every Sunday."

"What! In Burmese?"

"Yes."

"Let us hear how you preach!" It was a royal command.

Judson, swallowing nervously, began to declare "the perfections of God." The great throne room became profoundly silent, every face turned toward the speaker as his powerful, eloquent voice gathered confidence. He continued for several minutes. Then the king, smiling, indicated that his curiosity was satisfied.

Dr. Price had won admiration for his medical skill at the court, and Judson, believing that the Rangoon Mission would not now suffer at the king's hand, plunged into his work as never before. The mission prospered. Where Judson had formerly preached to a scoffing handful, he now had quiet throngs.

The Wades and the Houghs arrived from America to take over the Rangoon Mission. This left Judson free to use the grant of land in Ava given him by the king for the building of a *kyoung* (house of sacred characters). But Judson had to wait in Rangoon ten months for the return of Mrs. Judson from America, where Dr. Price had sent her to recover her health. During that wait, freed by the Wades and the Houghs from all the burdens of the mission save his preaching, he completed his translation of the New Testament.

Mrs. Judson returned radiantly well, and together they opened the mission at Ava. Here Judson preached every Sunday, and Mrs. Judson taught in their school for girls. The climate in Ava was often 110 degrees in the shade and so humid that the inside walls of their house dripped day and night. Both Mr. and Mrs. Judson came down with wild fevers.

Without much warning, and certainly with no hint that it would in any way affect the mission, war broke out between the British and the Burmans over the possession of Chittagong. All male *kala-pyoos* (white strangers), regardless of nationality, were arrested as "enemy aliens" and thrown into the death prison at Ava. Judson lay eleven months in irons in Let-ma-yoon-taung (Hand, Shrink Not) Prison, so named after the old edict given the first jailer, "Thine eye shall not pity and thine hand not spare."

This prison had not been washed or even swept out in a decade. The temperature in the windowless cellar den was always 100 degrees, the stench unspeakable. The fourteen-pound irons on the ankles and the fettered wrists of the prisoners prevented any relief from the swarms of mosquitoes that feasted on their naked flesh.

Judson was at that time thirty-six years old and much debilitated by his recent seizures of fever. He would surely have died had not his wife Ann come daily with food and water and, through bribery of the jailers, got him permission to walk occasionally as well as he could, inch by inch with iron-bound ankles, in the prison yard.

Perhaps no greater insight into the motivation of this man's life, his will to endure and serve, can be given than the fact that his concern for his wife, his newborn baby, and the manuscript translation of the New Testament was greater than his concern for himself. Ann could bring the baby on most of her daily visits, which, she assured him, God would give her strength to make.

But the manuscript? Where could it be harbored? Twice the mission home had been raided—it would not long be safe there. Judson himself must have it. Ann sewed it purposefully into a hard and uncomfortable pillow. The pillow was so unattractive that when she finally brought it to the prison she knew she had accomplished her objective, for "even the jailers had no thought of stealing it." On this pillow Judson lay, often in pain and delirium, for eleven months of unremitting misery.

The day he was removed and bound by iron rings to the long line of prisoners, he wept so wildly for the dirty pillow that the prisoner in front of him and the prisoner behind him concluded he had lost his reason. Jeering, the jailer sadistically ripped the pillow and tossed it in the prison yard, and then whipped his chained gang to a standing position for their ten-mile death march. On bleeding feet, moaning for water, blinded by the scorching tropical sun, they staggered and fell and came at last, some dying, most half-dead, to the country prison at Oungpen-la, where Judson remained seven months in fetters awaiting execution.

Suddenly a royal order came through for Judson to be

unbound and sent with guards to the Burmese camp to act as translator and interpreter. His captors condescended to tell him that his wife and baby were safe. Of the "pillow" that he entreated them to try to trace, they scornfully said they knew nothing and cared less.

In the camp, Judson served, unbound now but heavily guarded, until the Burmans conceded they had lost the war. When the time of peace negotiations came, Sir Archibald Campbell, General of the British Army, demanded that the linguistically skilled Judson be sent to him.

Of that voyage to freedom, Judson wrote, "What do you think of floating down the Irrawadi on a cool, moonlight evening with your wife by your side and your baby in your arms, free—all free! But you cannot understand it—it needs a twenty-one months' qualification, and I can never regret my twenty-one months of misery when I recall that one delicious thrill. I think I have a better appreciation of what heaven may be ever since."

Practically the whole of the English camp turned out to welcome the tall, gaunt missionary who limped painfully and who would carry to his grave the scars of the biting irons on his ankles. The reception of Mrs. Judson was also an event, for most of the English soldiers had not seen a white woman's face for more than a year. One of the British officers in the medical corps wrote, "Hers was the face of a saint . . . pale, very pale, with that expression of deep and serious thought that speaks of the strong and vigorous mind within the frail and perishing body. . . . When I looked my last on her mild, worn countenance, I felt my eyes fill with prophetic tears. . . ."

The peace treaty was signed on February 24, 1826, and

the Judsons returned to Rangoon on March 21. There they found the mission completely broken up, for the Wades and the Houghs had fled to Calcutta. But the faithful Burmans were still waiting in Rangoon and gathered around Judson to greet him.

"Oh, my teacher, that you should be alive! How good God is!" cried Maung Ing, one of the first three converts. "Twice the almond tree has borne its fruit and still my heart had mourned for you. All I had was the words of your heart to comfort me. No garment of yours to touch, no grave to bless with my tears. Even yet I have the foul pillow on which your blessed head lay."

Judson's voice was a hoarse whisper. "What pillow?"

"The torn pillow. From the prison yard. I picked it up and held it to my heart the day I reached Ava to visit you. The dreadful day I found they had all gone, and you with them, to the place of death."

"You have this pillow even now in Rangoon, O Maung Ing?"

"Yes, my teacher."

"Bring me quickly to where it is."

On his knees Judson tore away the filthy matting, but so well had Ann wrapped the manuscript in hard cotton and dried palm leaves and so tenderly had Maung Ing preserved it, that the whole manuscript, only slightly mildewed at the edges, rolled out safe before Judson's brimming eyes. So at last he had with him his wife and baby and his precious translation of the Bible.

But to this man it was not given to have all that he loved most. The hint of death that the young British medical officer had seen in Ann Judson's face and his "prophetic tears" were fulfilled. While Judson was away on mission business in Ava, Ann died of Indian fever and was buried in Rangoon nearly two weeks before the black-bordered letter reached him. Shortly after, the little child, Maria, died, too.

The sympathy of all America was aroused. Judson must come home, the American church people cried, at least for a rest! Surely he had given his all. America clamored to welcome home her veteran missionary. Brown University wished to confer upon him an honorary doctor's degree. England wanted to see and honor him, too.

British and American newspaper and magazine writers had spread the story of Judson's life in Burma throughout the English-speaking world. The adventure of the book in the pillow was known in many Christian households. But any desire Judson might ever have had for fame and recognition had been burned out of him. He did not go home until many years later, in 1845, when he visited in America for about a year before returning to Burma.

His sorrowful heart turned to the *Psalms* and he found himself translating them with a power of understanding that made them sing. He felt as if he were David. Since the songs had never been told in Burmese he was indeed a new David. Book after book poured from his pen until on December 29, 1835, the last page of the entire Bible in Burmese went to press.

But still Judson was not satisfied. For five more years he steeped his mind in Burmese prose and poetry. Surrounded now by Burmese assistants and transcribers, calling for corrections and suggestions from each of his missionary contemporaries as fast as they came to Burma and acquired the language, he revised and rewrote at the rate of thirty verses a day. The revision that satisfied him was completed in 1840 and distributed throughout the land.

The beauty of its strongly idiomatic words arrested scholar and layman alike. Buddhist monks read it, pacing in tamarind gardens before the pagodas of Gautama Buddha. They marveled at its literary perfection, its compelling truth.

Judson completed a long, rich life, full of sacrificial service for Burma to the very end. Before he died he saw his translation itself translate the lives of a generation of Burmans from Buddhist negation to Christian purpose. Through the Bible in their own tongue, the Burmans first tasted the gospel of the affirmation of life. Today that gospel is supplanting the philosophy of nullification of life on which the culture of the Burmans has rested for centuries.

7

No Trespassing

THE American sea captain, Blakeman, had tried everything he could think of to dissuade young Robert Morrison from the voyage to China. He had made his price a thousand dollars and then refused it when Morrison produced the money. He had given Morrison the run-around by referring him to Dutch and Danish ship owners who, the captain knew very well, would refuse such dangerous cargo as an inexperienced, twenty-five-year-old missionary.

On the day of sailing, in a last effort to rid himself of the persistent Morrison, the captain resorted to burning sarcasm.

"And so, Mr. Morrison, you really expect that you will make an impression on the idolatry of the great Chinese Empire?"

"No sir," replied Morrison, "but I expect God will."

Impressed, the captain said not a word more and the ship *Trident* moved out of New York Harbor at noon with Morrison hidden aboard.

Although Morrison was an Englishman and sponsored by the London Missionary Society, he had had to come to New York to get a ship for China because no British ship would give him passage. The East India Company owned all the British vessels that called at Canton, China's only open port in 1807, and the company had a policy of hostility toward missionaries. It adhered strictly to the Chinese law barring "foreign religionists," in order to protect its own precarious commerce there.

Morrison's assignment was "the acquisition of the Chinese language and the translation of the Scriptures into the Chinese tongue." This in itself would have been a task worthy of a mental giant. There was, however, an added complication that made the assignment suicidal. A Chinese law then in effect decreed, "From this time forward, such Europeans as shall privately print books and establish preachers who shall propagate their religion shall have this to look to: the chief or principal one shall be executed. . . ."

No wonder Blakeman hid the identity and purpose of his missionary stowaway! After a voyage of one hundred and thirteen days around Cape Horn and across the Pacific, Blakeman safely smuggled Morrison into Canton.

While studying medicine and astronomy in London, Morrison had lived with a Chinese scholar who taught him a little of the language and the customs. Nothing his teacher had said, however, had prepared Morrison for the life that the "ocean men," as the white traders were called, had to live in the thirteen rows set aside for them outside the walls of Canton. They could not live there more than the six months' trading season each year and were re-stricted to a plot of land about one thousand feet long and seven hundred feet wide, fronted by the Pearl River and backed by the high city walls. Here were located English, Dutch, and American warehouses and dwellings.

Outside this area, beyond the walls leading into the city, white merchants and sailors could not go, under penalty of seizure. They could employ no Chinese servants in their houses and were not permitted to bring their wives and children into the settlement. Nor could they ride in sedan chairs as the Chinese merchants did. When the six months were up, they went aboard the waiting vessels and sailed for other lands or to the Portuguese-held island of Macao in Chinese waters. All this was the elaborate Chinese system for protecting China from "foreign devil" invasion and influence.

Fearful of detection and because the traders lived on a staggering scale of self-indulgence in drink, food, and dress, Morrison learned to cook for himself the cheaper Chinese food. He lived rent free but alone, in an aban-doned French warehouse. He ate with chopsticks, grew long nails and a pigtail, and wore a Chinese coat and thick shoes.

On one point, however, Morrison did not pinch pennies; that was the matter of paying his native teachers. At the time there was another law in China that decreed that any Chinese caught teaching a foreigner the language would be put to death by slow torture. Morrison persuaded two Chinese scholars to take this risk. By day and night these men slipped in and out of the warehouse in the "place of the thirteen *hongs* [rows]" to teach him the language. Stealthily they brought Chinese books, papers, and pencils. One of these men lived in such dread of death by slow torture that wherever he went he carried with him a small vial of poison to end his own life quickly should his business with Morrison be discovered.

When the six months' trading season in Canton closed, Morrison abandoned his Chinese disguise and went to Macao. Here he could find no one at any price who dared to teach him. He worked in terrible loneliness and in continual fear of apprehension by both the Portuguese and the Chinese authorities. "I know," he wrote to the London Missionary Society, "that the labors of God's servants in the gloom of the dungeon have illumined succeeding ages, and I am cheered with the hope that my labors in my present confinement will be of some service in the diffusion of Divine Truth amongst the millions of China."

In order to be able to return to Canton at all, Morrison had to accept a job as Chinese translator for the East India Company's factory. Besides the routine correspondence and the eternal, slow-going, over-the-counter Chinese trading that he handled daily, he was encouraged by the company to work on an Anglo-Chinese dictionary and a Chinese grammar. By night he turned to the Bible. He made the translation in High Wenli, the literary language of Old China, considered one of the most difficult linguistic studies in the world.

By September of 1809 he had completed *The Acts* and hired Chinese printers whom he paid well out of his company earnings to print one thousand copies from hand-made wooden blocks. False labels were pasted on the covers of the books and these were then distributed free to Chinese booksellers who sold them willingly enough for small sums, since they netted 100 per cent profit.

Preparing for the annoying sojourn back to Macao, Morrison buried the blocks in Canton to prevent their discovery in his absence. When he returned, he found they had been demolished by a new and hitherto un-suspected enemy—white ants.

In spite of all these trials he published the entire New Testament in 1814, plugged away at his dictionary, and finished his grammar. The London Missionary Society was so delighted with his work that they sent him a colleague, William Milne, whose company the lonely Morrison en-joyed for only eighteen days. Milne was ordered out of Macao and forbidden to enter Canton. He went off to found a mission in Malacca where Morrison and he dreamed that some day they would open a Chinese col-lege and set up a mission press. Milne took two thousand copies of the New Testament with him for distribution among the Chinese-speaking inhabitants of the islands he would touch in passage.

Things began to look up. News came that the Bengal government was interested in publishing the Chinese grammar. The East India Company sent out a printer with a press and types for the publication of the dic-tionary. But this was too good to last. The Chinese print-ers working on the dictionary were seized, and govern-ment officers carried off some of Morrison's manuscript and Chinese type.

That was not all. Someone in the London Missionary Society got overenthusiastic about Morrison's work, talked it up, and even displayed some copies of the fascinating book. This came to the attention of the East India Company officials in London, who gazed with horror on the published copy of the New Testament in Chinese— done by one of the employees. Morrison received, as fast as the next ship could carry it, a letter telling him that his services were no longer needed. The letter was abrupt and to the point, since "serious mischief may possibly arise to the British trade in China from these translations." But the Canton office could not afford to lose so excellent a translator and kept him at his desk by the old dodge of protracted and, in those days of month-long voyages, time-consuming correspondence on the matter.

"This," said Morrison, with amazing understatement, "is a very tiresome place. . . . I am under continual dread of the oppressor and more than that—the natives who assist me are hunted from place to place and sometimes seized."

In November, 1819, on the completion of the Old Testament, of which Milne translated ten books, Morrison wrote, "I think of Britain, what she was, and what she now is, in respect of religion. It is not three hundred years since national authority said that 'the Bible should not be read openly in any church [by the people], nor privately by the poor.' I remember this and cherish hope for China."

Morrison did not live to see Protestant missionaries accepted beyond the walls of Canton, but his hope for China was fulfilled not long after his death. Not only were Christian missionaries welcomed, but urgent pleas were made for more and more to come. Y. M. C. A.'s and Y. W. C. A.'s flourished in fifty-eight of the main cities. of China, and thirteen of China's one hundred and fourteen colleges and universities were founded by Protestant Christians.

Today, much of China is again closed to the missionary enterprise. In spite of Communist infiltration, however, and the departure from China of most of the European, British, and American missionaries, Christian influence is at work behind the Iron Curtain.

Karl Friedrich Gutzlaff, the Robert de Bruce of missionaries, didn't believe the "no trespassing" signs at all the ports of Japan until gunfire stopped him. One thing above all Gutzlaff desired to do. That was to get into Japan to learn Japanese, but the ports of Japan were so completely blocked that even a Japanese who left the shores was not allowed to return.

One day when he was at his home base in Macao, Gutzlaff heard of the arrival there of three shipwrecked Japanese sailors. They had been adrift in the Pacific Ocean for fourteen months in a rudderless vessel carrying a rice cargo, were dashed ashore near Columbia in Oregon, brought to London, and finally shipped back to Macao. Nobody knew what to do with them—but missionary Gutzlaff did, and he talked the authorities into believing him. He brought the sailors home, beamed on them as fondly as if they were gifts from God instead of international problem children, and proceeded to learn from them the Japanese language. Not very literate but very communicative, Gutzlaff's rough teachers gave him their all. His house became the final port of call for shipwrecked Japanese sailors. By the time he was at ease in the language and had sent a translation of the Gospel of *John* to Singapore for printing there, he had a family of seven men without a country.

Grimly efficient on the one hand and on the other tender to the point of sentimentality, he brooded over the welfare of his Japanese family. "Ach, you are homesick," he would often say to them, "but one day we will all see Japan. God will find a way for me to take you home." He wished, before going on with his translation, to visit Japan and enlarge his knowledge of the language there.

Somehow he prevailed upon the manager of the Canton Trading Company not only to attempt to land the seven Japanese seamen, a medical missionary, an American Bible Society representative, and himself at some port in Japan, but even to pay for the adventure. The men boarded the good ship *Morrison* at Macao, and Gutzlaff, away on a mission of gospel delivery, was picked up at Naha (now Okinawa) off the China coast.

On July 30, 1837, the *Morrison,* decks cleared of mounted guns, flying a white flag, with the seven citizens of the country clearly visible in the prow of the vessel, sailed into the Japanese harbor of Uruga. Gunfire greeted them. They were forced to speedy retreat. The try-and-try-again Gutzlaff urged yet another attempt at the port of Kagoshima. Guns blazed at them from that harbor.

On the way back, four of the seven Japanese came to Gutzlaff. "We wish to make a sign that we give up our native land; from this day forward we are Christians." Their lives and work thereafter proved them sincere. They learned to read and write with much skill and remained for years in Macao. Two became translator assistants to Gutzlaff, and two worked in the office of Samuel Wells Williams, who later became the president of the American Bible Society. Together they completed the translation of the books of *Genesis* and *Matthew* into into Japanese.

Gutzlaff's attempt to get into Japan was only a small part of his colorful career. He had started out as a German pastor sent by the Netherlands Missionary Society into Chinese-speaking Java in 1828. He learned to sing the language of a hundred tones and became so proficient in Chinese that he was one of four men picked in 1838 to revise Morrison's translation of the Bible.

In Singapore Gutzlaff converted hundreds of Chinese and in four years trained forty-eight of them to go as Christian missionaries into the interior of China to preach the gospel. He went on to Bangkok, the capital of Siam, now Thailand, mastered the forty-four consonants and thirty-two vowels of the syllabic-type alphabet—characters that looked like tortured hooks and eyes wearing umbrellas at an angle. Into this language he translated the New Testament and audaciously came back to Bangkok a couple of years later to distribute "twenty cases of Scriptures in Siamese throughout the land."

There was no nonsense about the aggressive Gutzlaff. "Hear the Word of the Lord, O ye nations, and declare it in the isles afar off." If that was what the prophet Jeremiah wanted, Gutzlaff was going to see that it was done.

And off he went to the Luchu Islands (now the Ryukyus) and Formosa to distribute Morrison's Bibles and tracts. He traveled up and down the Indo-China coast from 1831 to 1833 by anything going his way: British brig, American gunboat, Chinese junk, or opium clipper, skirting disaster from mutiny and wreck at sea and danger from seizure and plague on land, his one concern the cause to which he was giving his life.

A Prussian and an idealist, he was all things to all men; he could inspire weary translators, whip up missionary zeal in new converts, out-talk the slickest officials, and bring the toughest sea captains to terms. He healed the sick in the holds of ships and under the palm trees on the island beachheads. He treated opium addicts with medicine and strong doses of Christian psychology. He traveled with contraband dictionaries and religious books, as dangerous then as firearms, into a half a dozen ports of the closed countries of China and Korea.

Morrison wrote of him to England, "I have the pleasure to say that from Canton I am sending a box of the Chinese Bibles with Prayer-Books and Tracts, to the north of China, Korea, and Japan. Mr. Gutzlaff, late of Bangkok, takes charge of them."

Gutzlaff dared to make contact with the emperor of China himself, saying calmly in a letter to his missionary society, "I have sent a Bible and tracts through certain officials to the emperor of China with a letter urging him to give diligence to the study of the Bible." It was like Gutzlaff to take the fact for granted that the emperor would study the Bible and then to remind him sternly to be diligent about it.

Gutzlaff never got into Japan. He died in Hong Kong in 1851, three years before Commodore Perry's historic expedition opened Japan to foreigners. Had he lived, there is little doubt but that he would have gone with Perry as interpreter, a history-making task that was given to his close friend and missionary associate, Samuel Wells Williams.

Born and raised as a Jew in Russia, brought into the Christian faith by a Baptist pastor in New York, trained for the ministry at a Presbyterian seminary in Pennsylvania, brave and intrepid Samuel Isaac Joseph Schereschewsky ended up as an Episcopal bishop in China.

The closed doors of China began to open here and there in 1858 and one year later the gay and brilliant "Brother Sherry," as his American friends all called him, entered Shanghai. He set about at once acquiring the Chinese language, or, as he said, "I should say Chinese *languages*." His plan was to translate the Bible.

Why, oh why, should it have to be done again so soon after Morrison and Milne? When they had worked several decades before, there was no national language. From their narrow foothold on the fringe of Canton, they did not dream of the hundreds of dialects in colloquial Chinese. They had been aware principally of the several levels of language among the scholars. Morrison's and Milne's translation was done in the literary High Wenli. Schereschewsky wished to make a translation into Mandarin, the language of the capital city of Peking. Varieties of Mandarin spoken in different parts of China have since been combined to form the language Kuoyü, which is known as the national tongue, inasmuch as it is now understood by four-fifths of the 475,000,000 Chinese.

To make this translation, seven missionaries collaborated with Schereschewsky on the New Testament. He alone translated the entire Old Testament. He spent nine hours a day for eighteen months acquiring the language of which he wrote, "There are as many distinct signs as there are ideas, particles, and proper names in the whole range of Chinese literature. These amount . . . to some fifty or sixty thousand [picture characters]. It is true that one-fourth, or even one-fifth, of this number will be quite sufficient to answer all practical purposes, but think even of eight or ten thousand different characters to be committed to memory!"

When the new American minister to China, the Honorable Anson Burlingame, asked permission for Schereschewsky to accompany him to Peking as interpreter, the young missionary seized the opportunity. To get into the capital city and thus perfect his knowledge of the language was just the experience he wanted before beginning his translation.

By 1867, a momentous date in his life, he was in the fourth year of the translation. He had purchased a discarded Buddhist temple, cleaned it up, and opened his first chapel. This done, he turned it over to a colleague for three months and announced he was going to walk seven hundred of the nine hundred miles between Peking and Shanghai to marry a girl he had never seen. When he reached the Yangtze River he traveled the remaining two hundred miles by an American gunboat. China then had no railroads, and travel by cart was slower than the energetic Schereschewsky feet.

A missionary friend in Shanghai had written him of the arrival there of a good-looking young American writer, Susan M. Waring. She had given up a successful literary career with *Godey's Lady's Book*, the most popular woman's magazine of the day in the United States, to become a missionary-teacher in China.

Schereschewsky made a beeline for the Nelsons' mission home in Shanghai where he thought he would find the girl. He arrived breathless on the doorstep and demanded, "Where is she?"

"Who?" asked Mrs. Nelson, staring at Brother Sherry's flying black beard and wild gray eyes.

"Miss Waring!" he cried with an impatient gesture.

"Why, I didn't know you knew her—she didn't mention it."

"I don't know her, but I'm going to marry her."

Unfortunately, there is no record of what he said to Susan when they met that night, but whatever it was, it worked. He returned to Peking in less than three months with the glamorous Miss Waring as his wife.

Schereschewsky completed the Mandarin Old Testament in 1873. Combined with the New Testament in which he had assisted, it was published by the American Bible Society. One of their representatives in China wrote, "No one not a missionary to China can understand what this work meant and will mean through all time to the church of Christ in that land. It gave a new impetus to all forms of missionary work and enabled the churches of all denominations in Mandarin-speaking China, so recently opened to them, to train an efficient native ministry and raise up an intelligent church."

It was also said of Schereschewsky twenty-five years after the publication of this Bible, "No man of that day equaled him in idiomatic command of the spoken Mandarin." Before he died he could speak and read twenty languages—at this time he was master of Russian, German, English, Greek, Hebrew, three Chinese languages, and Mongolian.

In 1875 Schereschewsky's board of missions, meeting in New York City, were listening to a report by the Bishop of Pennsylvania. "Great things," he said, "have been done by our mission in China. Schools have been established, churches erected, parishes organized, a native clergy and catechists trained, a religious literature started into being, and the Word of God translated. . . . But much of this will be lost . . . if the present headless state of the mission is permitted to continue." Two days later "Brother Sherry" was appointed Bishop of Shanghai.

One of the first things he did as bishop was to open a college, the first in China. On April 4, 1879, the cornerstone of St. John's College was laid. In September, four instructors and sixty-two students moved in to study modern science, theology, Chinese classics, and the English language. Several years later, medicine was added to the curriculum. The introduction of English, on which the bishop insisted despite protests, became a pattern for all subsequent colleges in China. The practice has resulted in a generation of educated Chinese whose knowledge of English keeps them abreast of Western arts, sciences, and politics.

In June of 1881, Schereschewsky asked to be relieved of his duties as bishop in order to make a translation of the Bible into Easy Wenli, "the language of literature among one-fourth of the human race." The board of missions said they could not spare him from the administrative duties he was performing so well. Stubbornly, Schereschewsky tried to fulfill these duties and at the same time carry out his own translation plans. He paid a terrible price for this. In a weakened condition from overwork and chronic fatigue, he was stricken with "sunstroke" (more probably poliomyelitis), which resulted in complete paralysis of the four limbs and loss of the power of speech. He was rushed by steamer to a specialist in Paris and, failing to find help there, to another in Geneva.

Four years later, in spite of the world's best medical aid, the bishop had recovered only his powers of speech. But he had adjusted so bravely to his invalid life that he began again to manifest the old Schereschewsky gaiety. He bought a riding chair for invalids that, attached to a cyclists' saddle, the advertisement said, "could be pedaled at the rate of 35 miles in 4 hours and 10 minutes." The first thing he did with this chair, aided by the Swiss manservant who took care of him, was to break the advertised record by going forty miles in four hours!

Schereschewsky lived in a wheel chair for twenty-one years, his legs so paralyzed he could not walk, his arms so paralyzed he could not move them enough even to write. Yet during these two decades this "helpless" man revised his translation of the Mandarin Old Testament, translated the entire Bible into Easy Wenli, completed reference Bibles in both languages, and left the beginnings of a

Mongolian dictionary. All this he did with the aid of a typewriter on which he could not type with more than the middle finger of his right hand. On his bad days, and he had many of them, he would grasp a little stick or pencil in his fist and tap the keys of the typewriter with that. No wonder the Easy Wenli translation is called the "One-finger Bible." Nor did a wheel chair prevent Schereschewsky from travel. He returned to live in China, visited Japan, and died in Tokyo at the age of seventy-two years.

The last recorded words of this brave man, as he sat, "grand as some old Levite," in the chair to which he had been so long a prisoner, were, "It is well; it is very well."

8

Babel Unscrambled

ROBERT SOUTHEY, poet laureate of England, published in 1809 an article in praise and defense of three self-educated men in India whose fame as Bible translators was viewed with skepticism by Oxford and Cambridge scholars. "These 'low-born and low-bred mechanics,'" wrote Southey, quoting the snobbish critics, "have translated the whole Bible into Bengali and have by this time printed it. They are printing the New Testament in Sanskrit, Oriya, Marathi, Hindustani, Gujarati; and are translating it into Persian, Telinga, Kanarese. . . . Extraordinary as this is, it will appear still more so when it is remembered that of these men one was originally a shoemaker, another a printer at Hull, and the third the master of a charity school at Bristol. . . . In fourteen years they have done more to spread the knowledge of the Scriptures among the heathen than has been accomplished or even attempted by all the world beside!"

The shoemaker of this trio of "low-born and low-bred mechanics" was William Carey, the first British missionary to India. In 1793 he and his family had been taken quietly into Bengal by a Danish vessel and a native boat. They settled in a village in the interior, a village surrounded by dense jungle, preyed upon by stalking tigers, haunted by slithering cobras. Everywhere they found caste-ridden men and women. By the end of Carey's first year in India, his little son had died, his wife was ill, his money was gone, and the villagers were still afraid of him. The vigilant East India Company agents had caught up with him and suggested he get out of Bengal or legalize his presence by going to work for them.

Carey took the job as overseer of an indigo factory. His contacts with the slave-driven coolies was their first experience in kindness and mercy at the hands of a white man. Talk with them was his first experience with spoken Bengali, which he had taught himself laboriously from books and trader talk.

By 1799 he had translated nearly all of the New Testament into Bengali. Given a dismantled second-hand printing press, he set it up with such reverent devotion that the coolies called it "the sahib's idol." The East India Company, relentless in their attitude toward any missionary enterprise, punned grimly that Carey had better keep the press an "idle." He was warned that he could remain with the indigo factory only if he gave up all notion of printing his New Testament.

Carey could come to no decision. Refrain from printing the New Testament after six years of work on it in suffering and exile? Or give up his only source of income, uproot his family, and accomplish what? Pacing the teeming docks he watched with homesick helplessness the latest ship from home unload. Little did he dream that in the hold of that very ship lay the turning point of his decision, his destiny in India.

A few days later, the most recent mails from England were delivered. In them was a letter from a man Carey had all but forgotten. It read: "Dear Mr. Carey. I know not whether you will remember a young man, a printer, walking with you from chapel one Sunday and conversing with you on your journey to India. But that person is coming to see you. . . . It is in my heart to live and die with you. . . . William Ward."

And in the next ship the other two members of that famous missionary trio, William Ward, "the printer from Hull," and Joshua Marshman, "the charity schoolmaster from Bristol," arrived fresh and enthusiastic. They gave to the worn-out Carey the transfusion of optimism that he needed. Before the East India Company could take any action against them, they got permission from the governor of Serampore, which was only sixteen miles out of Calcutta and was then under Danish rule, to set up a missionary community and allow the precious printing press to go to work. With their families, all three set out for Serampore by river on a dramatic date—January 1, 1800.

They established themselves in a common home, one for all, all for one. Marshman and his wife started a boarding school for European children in order to earn a living for all; Ward found an Indian blacksmith whom he taught to cut type from metal; and Carey rewrote and revised the translation, keeping a few galleys ahead of the greedy press. On March 15, 1801, the first New Testament in Bengali was "laid on the communion table of their church room in solemn consecration."

Back of that translation were years of work with *moonshi* (interpreter) and *pandit* (scholar). While Carey had found the written Bengali beautiful and expressive, the spoken Bengali of the coolies was bare and ugly, reflecting the bleakness of their empty lives. A little rice and a few brass pots to cook in were all they ever hoped to have. Outcastes, despised by all, their speech had no concept of words like "love" and "mercy" until he gave them these. He listened also to his three children, who chattered Bengali before they learned English, catching from their lips many of the idioms the *pandits* failed to, or could not, make clear to him.

How well Carey succeeded in the language can be guessed by the fact that in spite of the prejudice against missionaries, he was appointed the first professor of Bengali in the newly founded Government College at Calcutta for the training of young East India Company officials. He held this position for thirty years. Through his teaching he was able to influence the thinking of a generation of young Englishmen who had come to rule India and to effect many reforms.

Infanticide and *suttee* (widow-burning) were two of the Hindu customs that Carey worked against. Every year in the worship of the great Ganges River Goddess, it was the custom to throw new-born infants into the sacred river to drown or be devoured by crocodiles and sharks as part of the festival. Another practice was to put the living wife of a dead Hindu on his funeral pile, press her down by bamboo poles, heap it all over with *ghee* (melted butter), and then set fire to the whole thing. Carey's long campaign against these practices was won the day the British government in India finally declared them legal crimes. To Carey fell the honor of translating from Engglish into Bengali the governor general's edict making *suttee* a crime. After the new laws were passed, all Hindu funerals were watched and the Ganges patrolled at festival time. Gradually the horrible practices passed away.

Because of Carey's influence, missionaries, although still officially under ban by the East India Company, were admitted into Calcutta from both Britain and America. By 1805 the missionary colony at Serampore consisted of eight families. The Marshmans were making five thousand dollars a year on their school, of which they kept about two hundred dollars for themselves; the Wards kept the same amount from the profits of the press; and Carey supported himself on a like sum from his professorship. The rest of the earnings of each of these missionaries went into the enlarging of the mission, the printing of Bibles, and the growing payroll of language teachers, translators, and pressroom workers.

Carey's Bible in Bengali was read only by the literate lower- and middle-class Hindus. The high caste Brahmans would have nothing to do with it. Their reason, Carey decided, was that only Sanskrit, the literary language of India, was a fit medium for a sacred book. Therefore, Carey mastered Sanskrit and made the entire translation of the Bible in this language in ten years. Then scholarly Brahmans bought and read this Bible—it was now in Sanskrit, therefore sacred.

One day in looking over some new Indian dialects, Oriya, Gujarati, and Marathi, that had come to his attention, Carey let out a cry. "I can read these! They're the same root as Sanskrit!"

Marshman and Ward came running. Carey bubbled over. "We have the key to the vernaculars of the country! We must get help from the committee in England!" That night Carey made his first appeal to his mission society for money. "Given a thousand pounds a year," he wrote, "and we have it in our power . . . in the space of about fifteen years to have the Word of God translated in all the languages of the East." (Carey did not dream that even as late as one hundred years afterward, the total count on the languages of India, Pakistan, and Ceylon would be more than two hundred, twenty-four of them major languages spoken by at least a million persons each.) At that time Carey and other language explorers knew of only fifteen Eastern tongues. But as his work progressed and he and Marshman went further into linguistic research, they discovered forty-four and made, or had made, translations of some part of the Bible into all forty-four.

There was soon great interest in England, Scotland, and

the United States. Thirteen hundred pounds (then nearly sixty-five hundred dollars) was raised in Britain and thirty-five hundred dollars in the United States. On the night of March 7, 1804, at a meeting held in the London Tavern, the British and Foreign Bible Society had been formed. Their first foreign commitment was a plan to send the Serampore Mission three hundred rupees a month (then about one hundred dollars) for the work of translation.

Ward, who lacked the linguistic genius of the other two, turned himself entirely to the task of printing and the building of a "letter foundry" for the making of type. Carey and Marshman embarked on nearly three decades of linguistic miracles that turned Serampore into a Tower of Babel in reverse.

A day in Carey's life in 1806 reads like the log of a foreign language broadcasting station:

5:45 A.M.	Read Bible in Hebrew (private devotions)
7:00 "	Devotionals with family and servants in Bengali
8:00 "	Read with a *moonshi* in Marathi
9:00 "	Worked with Marshman on translation of *Ramanyana* (Hindu epic poem) from Sanskrit into English
10:00 " to 2:00 P.M.	At Government College teaching Bengali
3:00 "	Read proof sheets of *Jeremiah* in Bengali
5:00 "	Translated with chief *pandit* from College, *Matthew* 8 into Sanskrit

6:00	"	Lessons from a Telugu *pandit* in Telinga
7:30	"	Preached to congregation of officials and families at Mid-week Prayer Meeting in English
9:00	"	Translated *Ezekiel* 9 into Bengali
11:00	"	Wrote letters to England
12:00	"	Read chapter from New Testament in Greek

In March of 1813 Carey reported to the British and Foreign Bible Society that some parts of the Scriptures had been translated by him and others into Sanskrit, Bengali, Marathi, Oriya, Hindustani, Gujarati, Sikh, Telinga, Kanarese, and Persian and were in process of going through the presses.

A few days later, on the evening of March 11, Ward sat over his desk in the silent composing room, the workers having gone home for the night. Suddenly the smell of smoke drifted in. Ward jumped to his feet. A shelf of paper was on fire in the room beyond where twelve hundred reams of paper were stored. Clouds of smoke drove him back. Giving loud cries of "Fire! Fire! Fire!" he attracted the attention of the servants, who brought Marshman on the run from his home next door.

Together, they rushed about closing doors and windows. They ordered the servants to fill vessels with water from the near-by river. Ward clambered to the top of the storeroom. He broke through the roof and poured the pitiful jugs of water over the source of the flames. For four hours the whole community of Serampore worked over the smoldering paper supply. It looked hopeful until some stupid servant opened a downstairs window to water the fire from that point. The fire flamed up again. It leaped along the walls, through the composing room beyond, and ignited the litter of strewn galley sheets, cans of inflammable type liquids, and pots of grease. All night long the fire raged. Ward, Marshman, and the servants dragged the five presses out of the pressroom before the fire reached there. Tears streamed down Marshman's face as he worked. They had been too late to reach the precious manuscripts locked in the flaming composing room.

In the morning when Carey returned from a trip to Calcutta, the blackened ruins of the mission press stared at him. Three and one-half tons of melted metal, manuscripts of Scripture translations, grammars, and dictionaries in ten languages lay buried in the soaking debris. A loss of ten thousand pounds and three years' labor of the minds of scores of men!

What did they say—the three "low-born and low-bred mechanics"? In these days of impatience with small delays and petty disappointments, what they said seems hardly human. "We are cast down, but not in despair. . . . Traveling a road the second time is usually done with greater ease and certainty. . . . We shall improve the translations lost."

Leading Calcutta newspapers lauded the trio in headline stories, and the world heard about it. So aroused was public sympathy in England that it took only fifty days to raise the ten thousand pounds needed for the restoration of the Serampore Press. By the end of the year it had been rebuilt and was running twice as efficiently as before.

For another ten years the three labored together. Ward,

the one who could perhaps be most easily replaced, was the first to go. "It is in my heart to live and die with you"—Carey remembered those words as he stood helplessly by his friend's bedside, hardly able to believe that Ward, still so young and able, was dead. Cholera had struck suddenly.

The other two, whose knowledge never could have been replaced, worked on together until 1832. By that date complete Bibles, New Testaments, or books of the Bible in forty-four languages had issued from the Serampore Press, products of a teamwork of missionaries, Indian Christians, and *pandits* that has never since been equaled.

On the day of Carey's death, June 9, 1834, the government flags of British India flew at half-mast in honor of the man whom, forty-one years before, they had tried to hound out of Bengal. The man whose motto was "Attempt great things for God. Expect great things from God" had triumphed for himself and for all the missionaries who were to come after him. He was buried with royal honors and mourned by officials, princes, and scholars of the land he had loved and served so well.

One of the few manuscripts not prepared by Carey or Marshman that had perished in the Serampore fire was the first part of the New Testament in Hindustani. It had been made by young Henry Martyn, who had arrived in Calcutta from England in June of 1806.

This teeming city Martyn called "a foreign settlement upon the mudheaps." Its pulse of clanging gongs calling the Hindus to worship, the tramp of European soldiers' feet, the cobalt turbans of the men and the brilliant saris of the women, the smells of the docks, and the insolent cries of the beggars all electrified him.

Lost in amazement as he wandered about the narrow streets, he did not see the white man watching him or look up until the Northamptonshire voice arrested his attention. "Are you by any chance a new missionary?"

Martyn saw then "the kind and unassuming face" of the man whose picture and story he had seen and heard in England. "William Carey! You're William Carey!"

"Yes," smiled Carey. "Who are you?"

"Henry Martyn, new chaplain to the East India Company's officials and troops. But," he added quickly, "I don't intend to stay in Calcutta. I want to go to some new station in the interior."

"I don't want you to stay here either," said Carey. "Come to breakfast with me."

Over *loochis* (pancakes) and tea, they talked long, and Carey, who was not impulsive, learned enough about Martyn to say impulsively, "We need *you* at Serampore."

That evening Carey took him home and Martyn wrote, "I saw at last the place about which I have so long read with pleasure; I was introduced to all the missionaries. We sat down about one hundred and fifty to tea, at several long tables in an immense room. After this there was evening service in another room adjoining, by Mr. Ward. . . . With Mr. Marshman alone I had much conversation."

Martyn and Marshman became intimate friends. When Martyn could spare the time from his language studies and church duties he went with Marshman to hear him preach to wayside groups under the banyan trees and at the

106

bazaars. Marshman, too, did his best to get Martyn to stay. Here was a university-trained man whose classical knowledge of Greek and Hebrew and amazing linguistic genius would push the work ahead. He was fresh from Cambridge and only twenty-four years old.

But Martyn shied away from the Bible factory almost as much as he chafed at being held down to preaching. His sermons were delivered in English at the Old Mission Church and at St. John's in Calcutta to the many indifferent government officials who worshiped there. He preached so furiously and so greatly to their discomfort that in four months they gladly shipped him off to open a new station at Patna, then the second largest city in the province of Bengal in the northeastern part of India.

For six weeks Martyn journeyed on a *budgerow* (houseboat) towed by native boatmen and accompanied by his Hindustani teachers and native servants. Gliding upstream, he saw fields of hemp plants and silt beds of water rice and passed settlement after settlement of thatched shacks in miserable clusters under the mango and teakwood trees.

Evenings, after the boatmen had moored the barge, Martyn went ashore. He entered villages where no white face or blue eyes had ever been seen before. Here he distributed the supply of New Testaments and leaflets Marshman had given him from the Serampore stock and here he tested his Hindustani. On some occasions, he wrote, "All ran away when they saw me." At other times, in villages where curiosity overcame fear, men, women, and children gathered around him, talking timidly, then faster, and finally gabbling excitedly over his gift of books.

What a parish Henry Martyn found awaiting him in Patna!

His church was a barracks room with no seats and no protection from the tropic sun. Troops made up of the most reckless, mercenary adventurers of all Europe sullenly stared at him as they stood at attention for worship. The officials were no less resentful of a chaplain's being sent them than the soldiers. The civilian British judge, second only in importance to the general in charge of the troops, had married a Moslem woman and built himself a mosque. The population of Patna, predominantly a city of Moslems, looked upon Martyn in the streets with loathing. He was a white man, and they hated all the Western aliens with the bitterness of the conquered.

They came—troops, officials, and their servants—to Martyn's services on Sundays. The troops came because it was commanded. The officials came for form's sake. The servants came to carry chairs and footstools for the comfort of their masters, who listened to his preaching and then went off in their *palanquins* (enclosed litters) to take no more notice of him or religion until the next Sunday rolled around. And yet out of this flinty rock he struck living sparks. Within a month he had a major and six soldiers making Christian commitment and asking his guidance in reaching a higher level of living.

Martyn visited the troop hospital daily and conducted incessant funerals. The men in the regiments died like flies when fever swept the camps. Martyn lived in a bungalow in the cantonment filled with what could hardly be called the comforts of home: grammars and dictionaries in scores of languages, a crowd of jabbering language teachers, scribes, and servants, and an eternal round of sick and beggared guests whom he picked up in the streets.

Where Martyn found the time to study, to translate, to "build a garden and make alterations on my house for the expected coming of Lydia" does not bear thinking about, for he killed himself doing it all. Lydia Grenfell was a flighty girl in England whom he loved, who wouldn't say "yes," only "maybe," when he left. After a whole year's passionate correspondence and on the day the doctors in Patna told Martyn he had an advanced case of tuberculosis, Lydia's last letter saying "no" arrived.

Although the doctors told him that returning to England was the one chance to save his life, he felt that now there was nothing to go home for, and he went on working more feverishly than ever. He listened to the storytellers in the bazaars. With reed pen in hand he mastered the brush strokes, sometimes as many as thirty, required in each of the single characters of Oriental penmanship. Gradually he thus translated the New Testament into Hindustani. His translation did for the language of sixty million Indian people what Luther's German Bible had done for the dialects of Germany. Before Martyn's New Testament, no universal work of literature had been published in Hindustani. His New Testament became a textbook of that language, which is today the lingua franca of the greater part of India.

Martyn's teachers were Moslems. His principal aid, Mizra Muhammad Fitrat, was just as intent on converting Martyn to Islam as Martyn was in making Mizra a Christian. This meant that Mizra would shout over, challenge, and debate each line of Christian philosophy they translated. Over the Beatitudes, indeed nearly every other day, Mizra would fly into a rage and leave Martyn forever, only to return, repentant, in an hour, with a new argument. " 'Blessed are the meek'? How? When? This gospel requires a set of fools be born!"

And yet it was Mizra who, out of love and devotion to Martyn, faithfully retranslated the two Gospels of this translation that were destroyed in the Serampore fire. Martyn did not live to know about that fire.

Although his time was running out, Martyn began the study of Persian and Arabic. To assist him in these two new languages, Nathaniel Sabat, a wild and temperamental Christian, joined Martyn at Serampore. Sabat was somewhat on the order of Stephen Riggs' Eagle-Help, dressed always in gaudy silk with accessories of daggers, earrings, and dangling gold chains. "Think of the keeper of a lunatic and you see me," wrote Martyn, but he endured Sabat's blue-lightning temper for the sake of his brilliance in Persian and Arabic. In the end, however, his assistance proved not very useful.

To perfect the preliminary translations, Martyn asked permission to go into Arabia and Persia. The general of Patna, thinking this the last request of a dying man, speedily sanctioned the journey. David Brown, the head of the chaplains at Calcutta, wrote, "Can I bring myself to let you go? I confess I could not if your bodily frame were strong and promised to last for half a century. But as you burn with the intenseness and rapid blaze of heated phosphorus . . . your flame may last as long, and perhaps longer, in Arabia as in India."

Lacking the sympathetic companionship of a like mind

during that journey, Martyn wrote often to Marshman on the wonder of words. "I sit hours alone, contemplating this mysterious [business of] language. . . . How or by what magic is it that we convey our thought to one another? . . . Much as I long to know what I seek after [the philologic key to all languages], I would rather have the smallest portion of humility and love than the knowledge of an archangel."

The translation in Persian and Arabic done, Martyn started the long trip back, hoping to see England once more before he died. The Russian Bible Society at St. Petersburg had taken the Persian manuscript, which they published in 1815. The Arabic New Testament, somewhat revised, was published by the British and Foreign Bible Society in Calcutta in 1816.

But the tragedy of these dates lies in the fact that Henry Martyn died on October 16, 1812, at the age of thirty-one, in Tokat, Turkey. The trip back was too long for one so ill, so far from home. In the crowded city of Tokat there was no room in any inn for the sick white traveler. He lay down shivering and unattended in a stable, the sound of mule-bells in his dying ears.

The last sentence in the magnificent journal of this Keats of the missionaries was dated October 6: "There shall in no wise enter in any thing that defileth; none of that wickedness which has made men worse than wild beasts shall be seen or heard of any more."

9

Language without "Love"

"ONKA NA?" The American missionary pointed with his long slender finger at the kerosene lamp. "What is that?" he had asked in Mongo-Nkundo. Andrew F. Hensey, with pencil and notebook in hand, was beginning the task of writing down words that had never before been reduced to writing—laborious words spoken daily by the Bantu people of neighboring districts on the Congo River in Central Africa. The year was 1906.

The big black man with strips of leopard skin on his

hair and around his waist, bangled and barefooted, answered the missionary, *"Bosai."*

There was a bench on the porch where Hensey was working. He pointed his finger at it, *"Onka na?"*

"Bosai," said the chief, his white teeth flashing in a broad smile.

Bosai—lamp! *Bosai*—bench! Funny, thought Hensey, that right off he should have picked identical sounding words.

He turned to one of the chief's wives. Pointing at the banana tree in the mission yard he repeated, *"Onka na?"*

"Bosai." The woman was grinning, too!

Desperately, Hensey got up and went over to a small boy and pointing his finger at the woman asked loudly, *"Onka na?"*

"Bosai! Bosai! Bosai!" the boy shouted. He was shaking with laughter, and so were all the others.

Oh, it was a delicious joke! Ruefully Hensey had to laugh, too, for the laughter of the African is contagious, a thing of music and beauty. The only trouble was, Hensey didn't know what he was laughing at. It was a serious matter for him, for the whole missionary enterprise. If the answer to "What is that?" could only be *"Bosai"* and this word was some kind of joke among these primitive people, how could the missionaries break through to the language?

The Mongo-Nkundo language had no written alphabet and therefore no grammar, no dictionary, no book of any kind that Hensey could consult in his search for words. He had set about with his colleagues to record the language from the speech of the people. But *"bosai"* had them stopped cold. How could they ever learn a language where the name of everything was *"bosai"?*

It was weeks before Hensey found out by accident that *"bosai"* was the word for "finger." Every time he pointed, the Africans thought that he wanted to know the name for "finger" and that he was playing some kind of white man's game. When you point at something in the Congo, you stick your lower lip out at it.

And so Hensey and his missionary colleagues went around shooting out their lower lip at trees, birds, animals, and so on, accumulating words for the wonders of this fascinating land of canoe gypsies and hippopotamus hunters. That was fine for nouns, but how could anybody stick out his lower lip at a verb, an adverb, or an idea—like "sit," "quickly," or "love"?

Hensey wore himself out performing verb pantomimes. With their mouths wide open the Africans watched him sit, stand, run, sit, stand, run in rapid succession until they got the idea and cried, *"kitsanse," "emala," "ukumwa."* To get adverbs Hensey did it all over again with modifications, sitting *slowly,* running *fast,* and so forth. But the problem of finding words for ideas, words to express the Christian vocabulary that was beyond the experience of the Africans, was a tough one that took years of living with the people. The word "love," used more times in the Bible than in any other religious book, the words "hope" and "peace"—none of these seemed to exist in Mongo-Nkundo. No one ever said, "I love" or "I hope."

Even after years of patient recording of the words tracked down in jungle greenery, at dances in the village clearings, by the bedsides of those stricken with tropical sicknesses, in the canoe whose calling card at every shore was relayed by drum beat, Hensey still had no word for love. There was an expression he heard the Bantu mothers use in speaking tenderly to their own littlest children, "*ok'eefe'.*" And he asked one day, "*Ooi na ok'eefe'?*"

"*Bondele* (white man)," the mother said, "*ok'eefe'* means that I care for this little girl of mine so much that when I think of what is going to befall her when she grows up . . . it hurts me."

"Caring so much it hurts"—Hensey had at last the Bantu concept for love.

Since there was no writing by the people, the word "to write" was, of course, nonexistent. It was adopted from the chance speech of a small boy who watched Hensey writing with a stick in the dust of the street the bold outline of the first letter of the alphabet. The street was the scene of many an early mission lesson in reading and writing before slates arrived from America and before schools were built.

"Come quickly," cried the little boy to his loitering brothers. "Our *Bondele* is cutting tribal marks on sand."

The boy had said the word "*kota*" used by the "artists in blood" who cut into the living flesh of the faces and bodies of little children the intricate designs by which all men might know their tribe. Today, in Christian Bolenge and the surrounding districts, as a result of the work of Hensey and his colleagues, baptism and birth certificates take the place of the barbaric practice of tribal branding.

There were other problems to be overcome, deep-rooted fear and superstitions that obstructed knowledge. One day a fierce warrior called on Hensey, who happened to be writing a letter to his mission society. "What are you doing, Nkökö?" the chief asked. Nkökö was Hensey's African name, which, although he was then a very young man, means "grandfather."

"I am telling my people at home in Indianapolis, many, many rivers away, about the beauty of your country and the need of your people for the good tidings of Jesus. Two moons will wane before these words come to my land."

The chief banged his tribal stick on the floor, his fat black eyes rolled, and his nostrils widened in anger. "You are lying, *Bondele*. You cannot make paper run away and talk!"

"I will prove it to you," said Hensey quietly. "I will write on this paper anything you tell me and you may take it to the *Bondele* in the other house and he will tell you what it says."

"Write," commanded the old chief craftily, " 'Give this chief six oranges.' "

Hensey wrote down the request and put the note into the split end of the chief's stick. The chief was afraid to touch the paper with his hands. Waving it like a flag, the chief went next door to the house of the other missionary, who took the note, read it quickly, and called out to one of the family, "Give this chief six oranges."

The chief never got his oranges. He fled down the path to spread among his people terror of "the paper that could really talk!"

After Hensey and the other missionaries had acquired the language and long before any of the people had been taught to read it, the missionaries preached and told the great stories of the Bible. Seated at evening under the white tropic moon, around the fire in the village clearing, the missionaries passed on to the Bantus—as their chiefs and storytellers had for centuries passed on the traditional knowledge of the tribe—the message they had come so far to share.

Now it was the custom of Africans, if the story was good or the teller eloquent, to shout comments in praise or disapproval of the action of the story. Much as the English rabble, who sat in the pits of guild halls watching sixteenth-century Shakespearean drama unfold, used to yell at the actors, fight with each other over the sentiments expressed, and sometimes stop the play, the Africans reacted to the Bible stories. It cannot be considered rude or irreverent—anyone who has ever read to a child a story that unlocked his imagination will understand the outbursts of these Africans.

An associate of Hensey was reading one night from the book of *Mark* in his own Bible, translating orally into the Mongo-Nkundo language, telling for the first time the story of the arrest of Jesus and the account of his trial and crucifixion.

And they came to a place which was named Gethsemane and he saith to his disciples, sit ye here while I shall pray . . .

"Oh, the Innocent! The Innocent One!" An African woman rocked back and forth in the shadows, her sensitive mind alert to the danger, anticipating the tragedy of Jesus.

And straightway in the morning the chief priests held a consultation with the elders and scribes and the whole council and bound Jesus and carried him away and delivered him to Pilate . . .

"How could they!"

"Oh, the evil of it all!"

"That Pilate had better be good to Jesus!"

And they cried out again, Crucify him! . . .

"No!"

"Don't let them do it!"

"He didn't hurt anybody!"

And when they had crucified him, they parted his garments, casting lots upon them, what every man should take . . .

"Those black-hearted gambling soldiers! May the crocodiles await them on the beach!"

"May they all fall into an elephant trap!"

"May they set their right foot upon a sharp stake!"

And at the ninth hour Jesus cried with a loud voice, saying Eloi, Eloi, lama sabachthani? Which is, being interpreted, My God, My God, why hast thou forsaken me?

It was too much for them. The wild tears of those cruel and savage children of the jungle spilled over at the world's saddest story. The reader closed the Book. He could not himself go on but wept with them at the drama of Jesus' suffering that had never moved him more than at that moment.

When the time for Bible translation finally came, a thousand problems still had to be faced. "Wash me and I shall be whiter than snow," and "his raiment white as snow." How translate David's prayer for spiritual cleansing and the appearance of the angel who rolled away the stone from Jesus' sepulchre? These Africans had never seen snow! Nor ice! Nor frost! But egrets, great-winged birds, caught in gleaming flight under the tropic sun—they were the whitest white the Africans knew. "Wash me and I shall be whiter than egrets" and "his raiment white as egrets" are two phrases in the Mongo-Nkundo Bible that differ from ours.

Consider the wolves of Arabia that wander through the Old and New Testaments preying upon the lambs—how translate that in a land where there are no wolves? But the leopard is common, a constant danger to sheep and little children. And the passage from *Luke* reads in Mongo-Nkundo, "I send you forth as lambs among leopards."

"Candlestick, tent, desert, window, steps, and three-story houses" in a land that knows none of these things became "holder-of-torches, clothhouses, dry country, small door, short up-paths, and three-houses-high." Just as we have many beautiful idioms in English, Hensey discovered some picturesque speech among the Bantus. One is particularly eloquent. When you "kick" a man in Congoland, you "stab him with a footprint."

All these problems solved, the Bible translated, printed, and ready to deliver—but what good was accomplished if the people couldn't read? Side by side with the tremendous task of translation, Hensey had carried on the equally tremendous task of education. By the time the New Testament was ready in 1921, the children of the chief who had been afraid and had made others afraid to touch "talking paper" could read and write, and about a thousand of his tribe had also learned.

The day that Andrew Hensey left Africa to take the position of professor of African missions at the College of Missions in Indianapolis, eight hundred Christian Africans gathered on the shore of the Congo River to wish Godspeed to their departing teacher and friend. *"Yawe Fafa, otobatele enjiman'iso endoko"*—"God be with you till we meet again"—they sang, as only Africans can sing.

Hensey wrote of that farewell, which haunts him still, "Their hearts were filled with the Way, the Truth, and the Life. How often had I watched the first, the very, very first beams of light break in these faces as they learned of God in Jesus Christ for the first time. . . . And those eight hundred believers who gathered there that day were only a tenth of the membership of our churches in Congoland."

Today Hensey pays tribute to the many who aided him in language research and to the early work of translation done by Mrs. Royal J. Dye. He was also assisted in the final revision of the New Testament by E. A. Ruskin, S. Gilchrist, and H. C. Hobgood, missionaries all.

Nearly every major denomination of the United States, Europe, and Britain has missionary-translators today in many parts of Africa. To write about only one missionary-linguist from each of these denominations would fill volumes. The number of languages spoken in Africa is estimated to be eight hundred, nearly three hundred and seventy of which have been reduced to writing by missionaries. While not all the remaining languages are unwritten, it is believed that 50 per cent of them are still spoken only. The language problem of Africa is intense, divided as the continent is into forty-one countries and colonial possessions. In one country alone, Nigeria, fifty-three languages have been reduced to writing by missionaries.

In 1923, H. Stover Kulp, one of Professor Hensey's most brilliant students, aided by A. D. Helser and W. M. Beahm, reduced to writing the Bura language of eighty-three thousand people of northeastern Nigeria. These missionaries were helped in the mastery of Bura by a *Grammar of the Bura Language,* an incomplete and elementary work, but remarkable in that it was written by a self-educated Negro government clerk. The three missionaries, who had to introduce the English word "hope" into their gospel translations, have by their example and message made this foreign concept a part of the Bura language and ideology. Helser and Beahm wrote the first reading primers, which the Nigerian government later revised and adopted for bringing literacy to thousands. Kulp became editor of the first all-African magazine, *Listen,* which appeared in 1931. It was printed in English, circulated to all denominational mission headquarters in Africa, and then translated by native pastors and missionaries for use in the language of the tribe they served.

The first missionary to record an unwritten language in Africa was Robert Moffat, an Englishman who preceded David Livingstone to that continent by twenty-five years and whose daughter Livingstone married in 1844. Moffat reduced to writing the Chuana language of Bechuanaland, South Africa, and translated and printed the New Testament in 1840. From that time to the present day, the Bible has not ceased invading Africa.

Invading Africa or returning home? We need to remember that Egypt, one of the countries of Africa, was the scene of some of the most memorable events recorded in the Old Testament. Here Moses struggled with Pharaoh that the Lord's command, "Let my people go," might be fulfilled, and Joseph, betrayed by his brethren in Canaan, prospered in Egypt. It was from Egypt that the Septuagint, until recently the oldest known version of the Old Testament, began its long journey with the nomad Jews, the long journey in time and space that has encircled the world.

10

Calendar of Eventful Living

DOROTHY MILLER was graduated from Wellesley College in 1918 and shortly afterward became the assistant supervisor of high school study in Montclair, New Jersey, an ambitious job in a typical suburban town. It fitted the sedate opinion of Dorothy's classmates that she was "most likely to succeed." If the class prophetess had added to that, for instance, the prediction that Dorothy's picture would appear in an American magazine showing her dressed in the wrap-around, homespun skirt and blouse of a Mam Indian, her smooth long hair parted in the middle and plaited down the back, Dorothy would have been the first to cry with good-humored amazement, "Who—me?"

How she came to adopt the Mam Indian dress of Ostuncalco and learn their language is a thirty-one-year story that is still going on. It all came about because she married the Reverend H. Dudley Peck, with whom she went to Guatemala in the fall of 1922 to undertake a pioneering ministry among the Mam Indians. They went with camping equipment, medicine, a minister's library, and lots of pep to the mountain village of Ostuncalco in northwestern Guatemala. It was a region of corn culture, coffee plantations, malarial mosquitoes, steaming jungles, arid, bleak highlands, frequent earthquakes, and a swarm of jaw-breaking unwritten dialects.

Mr. and Mrs. Peck's hastily acquired Spanish, a language which a few of the Indian men could speak, saw them through the first stammering days and enabled them to conduct in an adobe hovel a Christmas singing service, dearest of recollections in the Pecks' calendar of eventful living. This service was unique. A handful of Indians, each singing in his own sweet time and tune—in spite of the restraining organ—expressed their joy in their first celebration of the most famous birthday in the world.

Index cards in hand, the young couple went up and down the mountain paths "pestering the villagers" as they wove their cloth for intricately designed shawls, as they ground their corn on the grinding stone, and as they worshiped their Lord of the Mountain whose face was rock and whose anger was chronic and implacable.

"Ti' t. bi ja'lu?"—"What do you call this?"—was the Pecks' first battle cry in the war they waged against ignorance, superstition, and fear. They wrote down what they thought they heard—*"ca"* (grinding stone and tooth),

"*c'a*" (bitter), "*ka*" (if), and "*k'a*" (boy). It all sounded hopelessly alike until their ears became sensitized by long and patient listening. Haltingly their tongues took on a talent for the gymnastics required of them by Mam explosives. After they were able to differentiate the four "*k*" sounds, they discovered other sound-effect problems.

They discovered thirty-eight different phonemes in the Mam language. Using the Roman alphabet as a base they increased the phonetic powers of the ABC's by following certain of the letters with punctuation marks borrowed from English. How impossible their task was can best be illustrated by taking the following simple Sunday school verse we all know and looking at it in Mam: "*Ku'n ictsun ttenju' tc'ujla Diosju' e'xjal, tu'nju' tsaj t k'o'n o'cxcu'jun tc'ual . . .*" That's how the Mam Indians say, "For God so loved the world that he gave his only begotten Son. . . ."

As soon as they had learned enough of this language that bristles with "*x, j, k,*" they began to conduct services and to think about doing a Bible translation for the growing church.

In five years they had succeeded in making a rough draft of the Gospels in the Ostuncalco speech. By this time, however, they had discovered twenty-two different dialects in the region. The Ostuncalco words for "a *woman* came to the well to draw water" meant to the people of Tacaná, over the mountains, "a *moon* came to the well to draw water." To do such a big job as Bible translation for one dialect, spoken by only several thousand people, seemed wasteful and inefficient. How then could they reconcile all the dialects of the 270,000 Mam Indians?

After three years of comparative linguistic study, the

125

Pecks called in to the translation table seven men and one woman, their best newly evangelized and literate Mam Christians, one from each of the main districts. Working together they attempted to harmonize the Mam dialects into one basic language and to cement it into a literature from which the Indian children would learn to read and write.

For three years this group met several times a year in translation sessions of two and three weeks each. They sat around a table burdened with Greek, Hebrew, Spanish, and English Bible versions, Mam manuscript, commentaries, and dictionaries, consulting them and the revised card file of dialectical words. A dozen times a day some one of the shaggy-haired Indian men in colorful home-dyed jackets would rise and humbly pray for "God's wisdom in this task."

During these eleven strenuous years of word hunting and translation, Mrs. Peck found time to teach her four small children, each at a different school-grade level, in their mission home. The Pecks believed that their children should enjoy an abundant family life before returning to the United States for an institutional education. Their experience proves that missionary children need not be deprived of a normal family life in the heart of a mission in a foreign land. The Peck children got a fireside education, and they held their own as perfectly adjusted American boys and girls when they left the family circle for their high school and college work in the United States.

Elinor Ford Peck graduated from Wellesley. She married a physician, and at present she and her husband are candidates for home mission service under the Board of

National Missions of the Presbyterian Church, U.S.A. William Jay Peck prepared for the ministry at the University of Göttingen in Germany and at Princeton Seminary. Paul Dudley Peck is also studying for the ministry at Princeton Seminary. And Dorothy Jean Peck, the youngest, is an undergraduate at Wooster College in Ohio. Like her sister and brothers, she also plans a full-time career in Christian service.

Besides the translation and family-education program, the Pecks also carried on full pastoral and clinical work. They got around by foot and muleback on mountain trails and, later, by car on the passable roads.

In 1939 the New Testament in Mam was printed by the American Bible Society. Before the official era of Good Neighbors, the Society campaigned for "Bible Brothers" in the United States. The generous response of Bible lovers made it possible for copies of the Mam Testament to be sold at half-cost to those Indians who could not afford the full price. The first lot of the attractively bound books arrived in Ostuncalco at Christmastime.

How faith in Christ had changed the lives of the Indians in hamlets scattered throughout the Mam tribe since the Pecks' first Christmas in Guatemala in 1922! Two organized Mam churches, comprising congregations and Sunday schools in nine districts, were carrying on a full program. Pablo Morales, a peon on a coffee plantation, had completed his studies under the Western Presbytery and had been ordained into the ministry as the first Mam Indian pastor. A Mam Bible Institute had been established for young men students. On the arrival of the revised, enlarged edition of the printed hymnal, which many of these students had assisted the Pecks in translating, they stayed up until two o'clock in the morning. The students refused to go to bed until they had sung through at least once every one of the hundred and fifty-nine hymns in the book.

It wasn't all "work and succeed" just like that. There were setbacks, disappointments, and danger. The second Mam Indian pastor to be ordained died a year after his ordination. An earthquake destroyed several chapels, but this only challenged the faith of the Christians to active campaigns for reconstruction.

One of the Pecks' most promising young converts decided suddenly to give up the girl to whom all the village had seen his mother carry the basket of bread and chocolate—the traditional token of good faith in the ceremony of "asking." The new young Christian wanted to give up the girl to whom he was "engaged" in order to marry another girl, simply because the second one could read. This was a serious breach of Indian marriage customs. The missionaries and their "foreign ideas," of course, were blamed.

The Pecks had other battles to fight. With quinine tablets and many deeds of mercy, they started a medical work that, with the help of a missionary visiting nurse, resulted in a growing weekly clinic at their community center, Tshoal Bey. Now a full-time missionary nurse carries on the clinic four mornings a week. Here some two thousand patients are treated yearly in the fight against malaria, hookworm, dysentery, and typhus. Through the extension department the clinic has been carried into several remote villages, offsetting the superstitious practices of the witch doctors. American missionary nurses and doctors opened a mission hospital and nurses' training school in Guatemala City and established country-wide clinics that are served seasonally by mobile medical units, in some of which the Pecks have cooperated.

One day at a Sunday service Mr. and Mrs. Peck were delighted to see among the congregation a well known village witch doctor, Chus. Although Chus had been taught to read by the missionaries and had even bought a New Testament, the pressure of his old cronies in the profession seemed to have stopped any further inquiry. That day, however, Chus expressed publicly his desire for acceptance into the church.

When his brother witch doctors heard of his confession of faith, they began to supplicate the god of anger to "bow Chus down." Shortly after this, Chus was stricken with a severe case of malaria and his new faith harshly tested.

The days of illness were tense for the Pecks, who took care of Chus. They knew that the sick man was aware that out on the hilltop the witch doctors had at sunrise sacrificed a rooster, scattered the feathers behind the idol, marked in blood the cut-in cross on the stone. They would then pray the Lord of the Mountain who had "bowed Chus down," as they thought, "to snuff out the traitor." Before it was certain that Chus would recover, he said, "I know that our Father God will keep me." His faith triumphed and today he brings a new message and scientific healing to his former patients, many of whom he has since brought to faith in Christ.

The New Testament was printed and in the hands of

the people, but only a few of them could read it. The Pecks felt they should now turn their attention to a mass literacy campaign. They started out with characteristic zeal, planning to plant "a reader in every home."

The first invasion of literacy, carried on by Mrs. Peck and several students from the Bible Institute, took place in the isolated hamlet of San Rafael Petzal, Huehuetenango, six uphill miles beyond the auto road. The Pecks set out for the hamlet. They wondered, as they hiked along, if the Mam farmers, all marginal livers, would respond to the opportunity to learn to read their language. And, provided they did respond, the Pecks wondered if it would be possible, with the literacy method used so successfully in many lands by Dr. Frank Laubach, to accomplish anything appreciable in the brief period of six days.

Mrs. Peck took over the women, ten of whom hurried through the chores of their household and the water carrying to be ready to attend the opening class. Squatting in the corridor of the thatched hut that had been vacated for the class, the women, with their babies slung in shawl hammocks on their backs, gazed raptly at Mrs. Peck's every move.

On the smoked panel of the hut door she drew with white chalk the picture of an alligator pear and beside it the word, "*oj*"—Mam for "alligator pear." They said and sang "*oj*" over and over. They had learned to read their first word. They learned two more in half an hour—"*toj*" for "in" and "*ij*" for "seed"—and ten more in the second hour. Cards containing only the words were then passed around to the group and Mrs. Peck next called on the women to read the words. They were hilarious and wanted to get to the men in the class down the path to see if they, too, were learning words.

At noon there was a gathering of the men, women, and children in the classes. It was like a *fiesta*—it became a *fiesta*. Everybody ate outdoors, the men around the knee-high tables, the women around the cooking fires, dipping up the soup with tortillas, drinking *atole* (corn water) from the gourds.

In the afternoon the picture-word vocabulary was built up and the test with cards repeated. Printed sheets were passed around containing the written words of hymns the Indian women knew by heart. As they sang from memory, Mrs. Peck's pointer followed each word on the hut-door blackboard. The choruses contained some of the words they had learned to read. When they recognized them, they shouted as if they had just met an old friend.

In the evening a worship service was held and a small crowd came. Mrs. Peck dramatized the reading by having the Bible students read from the New Testament as if they were a Mam family group sitting at home.

For five days more this went on. The evening of the last day twenty persons were picked at random from those who had attended the classes and given an opportunity to demonstrate before the others their ability to read the forty flash cards of words. These twenty quickly proved that they had learned to recognize every letter in the Mam alphabet. The forty words they could read had been chosen to do that very thing. Primers and New Testaments sold like hot cakes. Mrs. Peck lay down that night on her bed of pine needles strewn on the dirt floor of an adobe hut, thanking God that the experiment was working.

The news had spread around the outlying communities. Scoffers came from far and near to see what was going on in San Rafael Petzal. They came as to market, the women in long skirts and short ones, with plaited hair and ribbon-banded bobs, carrying on their heads water jugs and baskets of chickens and flowers (often in the same basket). The men came wearing big straw hats, leading donkeys, ducks, and small spotted pigs to sell in the square.

These were the colorful "mobs" Mrs. Peck referred to when she wrote, "On Sunday we shared their persecution, when mobs gathered around us in the market place to listen to the reading from a book. The missionary was called a beggar who had no husband, no home and sought support at the expense of the poor. Some contradicted, for they had seen her husband and the light-haired boys arrive with her and then leave. A stranger burst into the crowd demanding, 'What is that woman talking about? Tell her to shut up!' An Indian replied, 'No! She is telling us a good word in our language.'"

Before the literacy leaders left on Monday morning Mrs. Peck picked the man in San Rafael Petzal who had made the most progress and manifested some teaching ability. He was instructed to carry on the follow-up work in reading lessons with charts and the New Testament.

Mam reading campaigns were conducted anywhere and everywhere by the Pecks, on the cold mountainside, in the warm sugar cane regions, and in the coffee groves on the tropic slopes. Audiences of about a hundred men and women walked miles to attend the afternoon reading classes in their districts and stayed for the evening services. That first campaign has never ceased. The early goal of "a reader in every home" is part of the original purpose, "to make available the Word of God to the last Mam."

The emphasis on literacy work among the Indians precipitated in 1940 the adoption by the National Church Synod of a program of country-wide teaching of the ABC's. Mr. Peck was appointed chairman of the committee in charge of the campaign. He later became superintendent and now serves as corresponding secretary.

Today in Guatemala there are two hundred and eighty-five teachers at work in literacy. More than two thousand illiterates are enrolled in public classes, and lesson materials in six languages have been issued to more than six thousand illiterates. One of the best relationships between Christian missionary-educators and a Latin American government exists in Guatemala. Here literacy leaders in the missions go out armed with letters of introduction from the country's Board of Education to the mayors of the various towns where a literacy campaign is about to be set up.

The pioneering of the Pecks in 1922 led to this campaign in Christian literacy, which now is gathering such momentum that their aim "to make available the Word of God to the last Mam" may well be realized in the next generation.

When the Pecks first went to Ostuncalco, their purpose was "to make Jesus Christ known and loved by the Mams."

To that service, which knows no limits, every ounce of their imagination and talents was dedicated. Because they "love to tell the story," their life is itself one of the church's immortal stories. They take their place in the great company of missionary geniuses by right of their witness to their Christian faith.

Translators for Tomorrow

HOW do people learn to be translators? Tyndale, Eliot, Morrison, Hensey, and the others whose stories have been told here were the successful ones. But it took Eliot more than twenty years to learn the Indian tongue and translate his Bible. Today quicker results are sought. For hundreds of young missionary-translators, who want to share with peoples in distant lands the message of the Bible, special courses have been developed—courses in anthropology, ethnology, and branches of linguistics that include phonology (sounds), morphology (words), syntax (arrangements), and lexicon (meanings).

Such courses are given at the Moody Institute, Chicago; Columbia Bible College, South Carolina; and the Bible School of Los Angeles. There are also good courses in linguistics at Yale University, Cornell University, and the University of Indiana. Several denominations have their own linguistic training institutes at various points across the country. The Biblical Seminary in New York City often sends its linguistic specialist, Miss Esther Cummings, on short-term assignments as director and instructor in these smaller schools. Other institutions doing similar work are the Kennedy School of Missions in Hartford, Connecticut; Scarritt College, Nashville, Tennessee; and the Canadian School of Missions in Toronto.

A special school, founded in 1934, is the Summer Institute of Linguistics held every year at Norman, Oklahoma. Branches have been opened at Caron, Saskatchewan; the University of North Dakota at Grand Forks; Sydney, Australia; and London, England. Kenneth L. Pike, a director of the school at Norman, in addition to writing and teaching in the field of phonetics, has translated the New Testament into the Mixteco language of Mexico. Eugene A. Nida, now Secretary of the Translations Department of the American Bible Society, has also been a director of the Summer Institute for many years.

In these special schools the translators for tomorrow are put through a dizzy course of learning what various peoples around the world eat, wear, and build, how they behave, and why their customs are what they are. They learn that "p, b, t" are "plosives," that "fricatives" like "f, v, s, z" rustle the breath, that "pf" as in the German "pfeffer" is an "affricative," that "ch" as in church is an "affricative with a sibilant off-glide," and that the life of all spoken languages is one long round of "labial," "palatal," and "uvular" struggle.

The missionary students are severely tested as to their own knowledge of the Bible's many difficult texts in the light of biblical truth as a whole. They study the most scientific short-cuts in the acquisition of a language. They acquire all the latest modern techniques for reducing to writing a spoken tongue, and the various methods of imparting literacy to illiterates on a mass scale. From the examples of the mistakes and triumphs of the great company of famous missionary-translators of the past, the students learn to recognize some of the problems they will face on the field before they get there.

They discover that the Tarahumaras of northern Mexico sleep on skins on the floor, not on beds, and that the nearest piece of furniture to a bed is a bench. If they meet with a similar situation, they do not hesitate to follow the example of the translator who rendered *Mark* 4:21 into a warning for a Tarahumara not to "hide his light under a *bench.*"

The students find out that while the Totonacs of Mexico have no such household accessory as a foot-stool, they do in damp weather lift their feet off the cold dirt floor of their hut and rest them on "footsticks." *Isaiah* 66:1 then becomes in Totonac, "Thus saith the Lord, the heaven is my throne and the earth is my *footstick.*"

For those of the students who tend to feel a little irreverent about these changes made necessary by cultural patterns different from ours, the many similar adaptations made by Tyndale and others when our Bible first came out of the Greek into the English may be pointed out. For example, in the Greek, the texts concerning eating always depict people "reclining" when they eat, as the Eastern custom was to lie on couches during meals. Our habits, however, require tables and chairs. Tyndale wisely adapted the Eastern custom to fit the Western culture by using "sitting down" to eat instead of "reclining."

"The mind of missionary or layman," says Dr. Nida, "which frowns upon these cultural adaptations as 'changing the Bible' is in error, for how else can people understand the Word except in words that reflect something of their own culture and environment?" It is, of course, the genius of this Book that, no matter into what language or background it has been cast, it has never failed to hold its grip on the human heart.

Mistakes of translators, especially the tendency of some of them to be too literal in the rendering of English idioms, are cited for the students' examination. One example of the translation of our idiom "taste of death" is really funny. It was caught on the field. If it had passed, *Mark* 9:1 would have read, "And he said unto them, Verily I say unto you, That there be some of them that stand here which shall not *chew on a corpse,* till they have seen the kingdom of God come with power."

Some mistakes in modern translations are far too subtle to be detected by missionary-translators. But there is still another check to insure accuracy, the "informant." This is the technical name given to native aids in translating.

One mistake that got into proof puzzled a young Yipou-nou informant of West Africa very much. The centurion in *Matthew* 8:9 who described himself, "For I am a man

. . . having soldiers *under* me," makes himself perfectly clear to any English reader who knows instinctively the idiomatic meaning of "under." The Yipounou people, however, have but one meaning for "under." They, therefore, pictured the centurion as a warrior sitting on top of the piled up bodies of slain victims. The manuscript translation was revised to read, "For I am a man . . . who *goes ahead of* his soldiers," which makes everything quite Yipounou, since their captains do exactly that.

Many translators have found native idioms far more beautiful than our equivalent English expressions. For instance, the idiom of the Tzeltal language of Mexico for our words "to be sad" is "to count your heart"; if you are stupid, "your heart is closed." In the Luba-Lulua language of the Belgian Congo, reduced by missionary John Morrison to a written language, the concept for God is *"Ntabale,"* which means "always-wide-awake one." In Shilluk in the Sudan, the translation of *John* 3:30 ("He must increase, but I must decrease.") becomes sheer poetry: "He must come in out of the morning, and I must go in out of the night."

In Chichimeca there is no word for "bus," but from the description that the missionary gave the natives, they told him it would be *"gul' uswa' doa-ko'pu,"* literally, "a house that walks over the land." In Africa when a missionary described a telephone to an evangelist, he, in turn, told his people that a telephone is "a white man's animal whose tail when pulled in the interior makes him to bark on the coast."

The translators-in-training are told they must mingle with the people, attend the palavars that are the schools of folk wisdom. The missionary may never find words to translate our proverb about "jumping from the frying pan into the fire," but if he sits around the campfires of western Africa he will not have to wait long to hear the story of the man who was so afraid of the sword that he hid in the scabbard. He is taught that he must bring an open mind to the habits and customs that he might tend, at first, to dismiss as superstitious and even disgusting. Many a missionary who has gagged at the thought of his Christian converts eating toasted locusts or fried ants has himself, when famine or failure of food on a long trek drove him to it, become convinced that locusts and ants provide satisfying food.

The translators' problems are not restricted to words, written or spoken. Preparing a manuscript for transmission to the American Bible Society for printing is in itself a great labor. Translators are taught how to keep a concordance of key words, since it is not always possible to render a word in the same way in all places in the Bible. Variations, however, must be kept at a minimum. Sometimes a word used in the early days of translation has to give way to a more exact and better word discovered years later. The whole manuscript must then be combed to take out the old word and insert the new.

The labor involved in typing the final copy for the printer is in itself a task of months. With the manuscript must come a translation of any footnotes or translational helps used, for the study and examination of the American Bible Society's Translations Department. Before being finally mailed out to New York, all this material must be read for typing errors. This is a job that has meant for many a missionary and his wife several months of reading the entire Bible aloud together.

The work of the Bible Society, however, begins long before the manuscript is received in New York. Dr. Nida has found that great assistance can be rendered the missionary translators as early in their work as when they are first analyzing the sounds of the language or making a first attempt at translation. He often visits the mission field where translating is in progress to assist the missionary in his task. Such journeys have taken Dr. Nida and his wife, who aids in constant secretarial work, to forty-three countries, from the peaks of the Andes to the jungles of Africa.

Because he cannot visit all the missions in need of technical linguistic help, Dr. Nida has prepared several books to take his place at the translator's table, *Bible Translating, Learning a Foreign Language, A Translator's Commentary on Selected Passages,* and others. Regional conferences of translators, such as the one Dr. Nida attended recently in Guatemala, also help stimulate keener work. Here missionaries and nationals, some of them barefooted Indians, meet for several days to discuss translation problems and procedures. Nationals are used because they can produce the many sounds, they know how the words are naturally put together, and they can tell what the translation actually means to them. All this is done to make sure that when the manuscript is finally sent to the American Bible Society, the text is as faithful a transfer of the original into the local language as is possible.

When the Committee on Translations in New York is convinced of this, the manuscript goes to the printer. The strenuous task of proofreading and correcting follows. Then comes that glorious day, for the missionary and the people, when the first package arrives containing the Word in a new language—their own speech. What do they say, how do they receive the long-awaited book?

One story comes from the village of Elat in the Cameroons. The Bible's arrival had been delayed by World War II. Many of the books were lost at sea. One day, however, two thousand Bibles arrived to be distributed among more than one hundred thousand Bulu Christians. Priority lists of native evangelists, Sunday school teachers, and elders had been made. But there were not even enough to go around among these. Not knowing how to distribute them, the man in charge tossed the last few copies into the crowd who had assembled outside the mission infirmary. One of the old evangelists, stiff with age, became nimble in his anxiety to catch a Bible. He succeeded and held it close for a moment of thanksgiving to God. For years this old man's daily prayer had been, "Let me not die until the Bible comes."

The eagerness with which some peoples receive the Word of God is matched with the fierce hatred that others may have for it. Dr. Nida reports, "One translator was approaching a village in a steaming tropical jungle of Latin America. A small band of men met him. One of them stepped out and grabbed him by the shoulder, brandished his razor-sharp machete, and drew it across the throat of the missionary. Then he warned him in no uncertain words that next time he would slit his throat if the missionary did not leave immediately. The people of this village were determined to keep out anyone who would bring them the Book, which they had been told was 'the book of the devil.' "

"This incident," says Dr. Nida, "is not rare. The history of missions is full of the accounts of men and women who have been shot, beaten, and tortured because they dared to bring the Word of God to men who had not read and could not read it. No translator turns back in the task of giving the Word because it may cost him his life, not when other men have sacrificed so much."

It is no wonder that our country has pioneered in modern schools for missionary-translators. Nearly all our great colleges were established by our early church leaders for religious purposes. John Harvard, in 1636, founded America's first college "to save churches from an illiterate ministry." Dartmouth College came into being in order "to impart Christian knowledge to savages." This could happen only in a land whose founding fathers so loved the Bible and lived by it that they put upon the famed Liberty Bell the biblical words of a prophet, "Proclaim liberty throughout all the land unto all the inhabitants thereof."

"Our schools for tomorrow's translators," writes Dr. Nida, "are desirous of helping pioneer linguistic missionaries meet a challenge. We face the challenge of reaching the world with the Message of Life in a language which the various peoples of the world can understand and which, as their own, speaks to the heart and is in fact 'the shrine of a people's soul.' "

12

The Newest—
or the Oldest—Bible

ON September 30 the first printing of a million copies of a new book, a figure unprecedented in the history of publishing, had rolled off the press and was on sale in bookstores across the country. Within a few weeks the entire printing had been sold, and backlog orders for six hundred thousand copies kept the presses of five plants running day and night. The book has been hailed as a classic through all the avenues of modern communication: the press, the pulpit, the radio, and television. It has been furiously denounced by some people as blasphemous; it has even been publicly burned.

The pattern is historically familiar. The book, which is the perennial precedent breaker, the perpetual best-seller, the book, which has been passionately defended by men of all ages and publicly reviled and burned many times in many places, could be none other than the Holy Bible. But the amazing fact about this story and this Bible, setting it apart from all others, is that it happened to us in our time. The year was 1952 and the place, the United States of America. The Revised Standard Version is our Bible in our language, making history in our day.

If, as has been said, the King James Version is "a masterpiece," "a monument in words," "a noble inheritance and national treasure," how could it be improved? In 1611 when the King James Version was completed, it was a masterpiece *in the language of that day* and will always remain so. But the fact is that some men of that day refused to accept it and failed then to recognize its beauty.

"This Bible denies the divinity and Messiahship of Jesus Christ" sounds like yesterday's newspaper, but the statement was made by a London clergyman in 1611. "This Bible reflects the translators' opinions" sounds contemporary, but the statement is also dated 1611 when a chaplain accused the translators of having pandered to the King's interest in witchcraft by inserting terms that favored it. The Pilgrims in 1620 were still resisting the King James Version when they landed on these shores; it was not the Bible that traveled with them on the *Mayflower*. It took more than fifty years for the King James Version to become the revered Bible we know. The current resistance to the Revised Standard Version will die eventually, and it is easily predictable that the next translation—for it will be done again and again and again—will meet a similar fate.

Who decides to revise the Bible? Men like Luther, Wycliffe, Tyndale—all that host of the great company of men who have refused to let the message of the Bible sleep in obscurity or die of antiquity.

Tyndale, the man to whose translation the King James Version owes so much, once said to a learned doctor, "I will cause a boy who driveth the plow to know more of the Scripture than thou doest." And he did so, for his Testament was in the language of that boy. Should we do less? Should we ask the boy who drives a tractor today to learn the language of the boy who drove the plow, to conquer its Elizabethan turn of phrase and style, in order to understand the message of the Bible?

Languages are like rivers, restlessly moving through time and space, losing a little of themselves here and there, deepening and shifting and changing color and form. Although the Word of God is immutable, the English language has moved through 342 years of change since the publication of the King James Version.

In seventeenth-century England, and even in nineteenth-century America, "charity" had carried over from Jerome's Latin *caritas* the meaning of "universal love." The King James Version translates Paul's message to the Corinthians as "And now abideth faith, hope, charity, these three; but the greatest of these is charity." And Lincoln, whose mastery of style he himself attributed to his study of the Bible, in the famous final paragraph of his Second Inaugural Address used the same word with the meaning of brotherly love when he said, "With malice toward none; with charity for all. . . ." "Charity" was once an adequate English translation of the Greek word *agape* (love), but "charity" has lost its connotation of universal love and has come in our time to have the rather individualized meaning of "giving to the poor."

The word "communicate" once meant "share"; today it means "make known." The word "conversation" meant "behavior," today it means "talk." To "mortify" was not to "humiliate" then, but to "put to death." "Out of hand" meant "at once." And a man who was "quick" was not in a hurry then, he was merely "alive." There are more than four hundred words of this character that have been amended not to change so much as to use the language of our day to give the true intent of the message, as indicated in the oldest biblical texts that have come to light.

Not only are words left behind in time or changed in meaning, but grammatical structure, spelling, and punctuation have changed, too. In the Revised Standard Version poems, psalms, songs, hymns, and laments are attractively set up to convey the effect of the form and persuasive rhythm of Hebrew poetry. Quoted matter is set off by quotation marks, and italics—which mean emphasis to us but which were used in the King James Version to indicate that these words had been filled in by the translators—have been removed.

Even more arresting than the modifications of language are the findings of classical scholars and biblical philologists who have, since the seventeenth century, carried on unending study of the ancient Greek, Latin, and Syriac versions and, in addition, have made some startling discoveries about Hebrew words from comparative studies in the Semitic languages. Through the patient research of these latter-day scholars, obscure words have been clarified and human errors in an earlier scholarship have been corrected.

In the last fifty years the sands of the Near East have yielded the archeologists more than the treasures of the tombs of kings. In 1928 at Ras Shamra on the coast of Syria, archeologists explored an ancient tomb, which a peasant had stumbled upon while plowing his rocky field. They discovered Ugaritic clay documents dating back 1400 years before Christ. And a dictionary of the words of the deciphered clay inscriptions has added to the wonder and confirmed the truth of our knowledge of the Canaanites and Old Testament times.

In 1931, Chester Beatty, an American whose home is in London, was browsing in an antique dealer's shop in Cairo, Egypt. He purchased what he surmised might be manuscript, but it looked more like blocks of rotting wood. He turned the blocks over to experts at the British Museum in London. With mounting excitement the museum preparators separated page after page—the patient, nerve-wracking work of months—and finally they announced the incredible discovery: the most ancient Greek biblical manuscript yet to come to light lay before them. Among fragments of books of the Old and New Testaments were found nearly all the letters of Paul, some of them dating back to the middle of the third century.

In 1947 a nomad Bedouin boy explored a cave on a cliff above Khirbet Qumran on the Dead Sea. He found many jars in the cave and, as boys will, he broke some to get at the treasure he hoped to find inside. He was disappointed. What he found wrapped in linen cloth was not gold or precious stones but leather scrolls. The discovery came to the attention of scholars. The Syrian Orthodox Monastery of St. Mark's in Jerusalem, the Hebrew University on Mount Scopus, and later the Rockefeller Museum of Jerusalem purchased the scrolls. Examination revealed that one of the scrolls in this astounding collection was the book of *Isaiah* in Hebrew. Although there are hundreds of differences in spelling of words, grammatical structure, and evidences of mistakes of copyists, it is proof of the substantial accuracy of the text we know which dates from the tenth century. When archeologists reached the cave, they estimated that the scrolls had been put into the jars about the first century A.D. and that some of the manuscripts had probably been written in the latter part of the second century B.C., giving us for the first time biblical manuscripts that had actually been copied in Old Testament times.

Since the King James Version had been based on a few medieval manuscripts, the multitude of ancient manuscripts that have been discovered since 1611 made revision imperative. These documents have made possible the elimination of the accumulated errors of centuries of human failure in scholarship and in manuscript copying.

For example, *I Samuel* 14:41 reads in the King James Version: "Therefore Saul said unto the Lord God of Israel, Give a perfect *lot*. And Saul and Jonathan were taken: but the people escaped." Here is how it appears in the Revised Standard Version, "Therefore Saul said, 'O Lord God of

Israel, why hast thou not answered thy servant this day? If this guilt is in me or in Jonathan my son, O Lord God of Israel, give Urim; but if this guilt is in thy people Israel, give Thummin.' And Jonathan and Saul were taken, but the people escaped." Did the revisers make this up? No. Scholars, in going back to the ancient versions, discovered that when the scribe who had copied this verse came to the line that ended with the first "Israel," he had inadvertently skipped the lines in between and picked up his copying after the third "Israel." This is a very common failing that plagues typists and printers today.

All these factors made clear the need for revision. The work was authorized, and a committee was appointed in 1930 by the International Council of Religious Education on behalf of the forty major Protestant denominations of the United States and Canada. Since that time this Council has become the Division of Christian Education of the National Council of Churches of Christ in the United States of America. After many delays, largely due to the depression, the committee went to work in 1937 under the leadership of Dr. Luther A. Weigle, now Dean Emeritus of Yale University's Divinity School. The committee was charged "to embody the best results of modern scholarship as to the meaning of the Scriptures and to express this meaning in English diction, which is designed for use in public and private worship, and to preserve those qualities, which have given the King James Version a supreme place in English literature."

A few of the men on the committee were chosen for their distinguished competence in the field of English literature, some for their creative leadership in public worship or in religious education, but twenty-eight were men of renown in biblical scholarship. They came from more than twenty universities and theological seminaries in the United States and Canada. Since 1937 the committee has varied in size from fifteen to thirty-two men. Two of these, James Moffatt of the Union Theological Seminary of New York City and Dr. William R. Taylor of the University of Toronto, Canada, did not live to see the task completed.

The committee was divided into two sections—the New Testament and the Old Testament. An individual member would be asked to prepare a preliminary translation of a book of the Bible in his section. Copies of his translation were mailed to all other members for private study. The committee would then meet for seminar-type discussions. They met for two two-week sessions each summer and for about ten days during academic winter holidays, working together from 9 A.M. to 9:30 P.M. every day. During these discussions they analyzed the suggested translations word for word, verse for verse, chapter for chapter, book for book. Where there was disagreement among the ancient manuscripts, the most valid interpretation was used, and in some cases the alternatives are cited in the footnotes. After twelve years of work the Old Testament Section had completed a first draft of its project. All that remained for these hard-working, dedicated men were 909 single-spaced mimeographed pages of suggestions, controversial points, and questions to be settled!

The members of the New Testament Section spent 145 working days, and the members of the Old Testament Section spent more than 300 working days in face-to-face discussion—in addition to the countless days of independent translation and study of the translations of others, which they carried on at home. For this labor they received no recompense. Thomas Nelson & Sons, the publisher who had agreed to print the book and bear most of the expense of preparation, was granted exclusive rights to publish the Revised Standard Version for ten years, after which it will be open to other publishers. The copyright is held by the Division of Christian Education of the National Council of Churches.

On April 3, 1951, Thomas Nelson & Sons set to work on the gigantic task of typesetting, proofreading, printing, and binding an initial installment of one million copies of the Bible in English. To accomplish so unprecedented a venture in commercial printing, 1,000 tons of paper, 2,000 gallons of ink, 140 tons of binder's board, 10 tons of type metal, 71 and one-half miles of 40-inch wide cloth, and 18,750,000 yards of thread were needed. Although each Bible is only one and one-half inch thick, if the million copies were stacked one upon the other, they would tower twenty-four miles into the air, higher by one hundred times than the Empire State Building, the tallest skyscraper in the world.

The publication date was finally announced as September 30, 1952. Governors of more than twenty states issued proclamations declaring September 28 to October 5 as "Christian Education Week," the programs to be centered about the advent of the Revised Standard Version of the Bible. More than 1,500,000 people attended 3,418 Bible observances in the United States, Canada, Hawaii, and the Canal Zone. Chaplains with the United States Armed

Forces in Germany, Japan, and Korea led special services commemorating the new version.

The Bible was a lead feature in tabloids across the country. It was highlighted in trade journals, national magazines, and house organs. It made the newsreels and all the major networks. And *Life* went to the mammoth outdoor Bible observation in Port Arthur, Texas, where many businesses closed early that afternoon so that employees and their families could attend the interracial, interdenominational service that attracted 7,500 people.

On the same day, September 30, the United States Post Office issued a stamp commemorating the 500th anniversary of the publication of the Gutenberg Bible. The Library of Congress exhibited to the public their famous and priceless Bibles. Millions who could not journey to the Library of Congress to see for themselves the first book ever printed with movable types cast in molds saw it in their living rooms. The National Broadcasting Company televised the Gutenberg Bible from its Washington studios. To protect that rare Bible the network took out the largest one-day insurance policy ever issued on any book—for $300,000.

So much for physical bigness, impressive statistics, the nervous fanfare of our day. There is another kind of grandeur here that overwhelms the heart and fills the mind.

It is still the old, old story, standing invincible before all that modern science has discovered. All that the tools of scholars and archeologists have yielded has challenged not a word of its truth, its message. Rather has each discovery illuminated for us the depth to which this message has penetrated the history of mankind. Only in a very limited sense is this our modern Bible. It is, indeed, our most traditional Bible, for some of the readings of the Revised Standard Version reach deeper into time and the heart of ancient man than the mind of modern man can comprehend with ease.

This revision was done in love by all that host of dedicated collaborators from Wycliffe to Weigle, and all the monumental labor of the love that went into it shines out of it. It will be read aloud, it will be sung to music yet unheard, and out of this generation to whom it tells the old, old story in all the beauty and dignity of their living language will come a fresher, more heroic literature and art than we have yet seen in our time. And religion will flourish, for the root of faith is alive in our land once more —the old, old story is made new again.

13

My Words
Shall Not Pass Away

IN a tiny village in eastern Poland a colporteur had left a single copy of the Bible. Converted through reading it and wishing to share its message, the owner memorized several chapters and passed it on to another. He, in turn, did likewise and passed it on again. As the Bible traveled from hand to hand, it became the most prized possession in the community.

By the time the colporteur made his next visit, two hundred new Christians in the village came to greet him.

They showed him the tenderly preserved but well worn Bible—still going the rounds.

The colporteur then and there held the first service of public worship in that village. Since so many of the new Christians seemed to be able to quote texts freely, he suggested the service be opened by volunteer recitation of some loved verse of Scripture.

One man arose and asked, "Do you mean a verse or a chapter?"

Astonished, the colporteur inquired, "Are there people here who can recite a chapter of the Bible?"

To his amazement the colporteur found that among them these two hundred villagers knew practically the entire Bible by heart.

In a day and culture far removed from the time of the psalmist who sang, "Thy word have I hid in my heart," the modern fulfillment of that testimony still goes on. It goes on around the world, not only through the missionary-translator and the colporteur distributor but also through the Bible societies of many lands.

In 1939 British, American, Scottish, Netherlands, Norwegian, and French Bible Societies met together for the purpose of forming an international Bible society, but war intervened. Not until 1946 was the plan for a United Bible Societies realized. Today the members represent the Bible societies of twenty-five countries. Their purpose is to work together to further the world-wide circulation of the gospel.

The accelerated need for biblical translation, publication, and distribution—caused by the spread of adult literacy in many parts of South America, India, and Africa—

has made the experience and help of the United Bible Societies invaluable to new and younger national members. The headquarters of the United Bible Societies in London serves as a center of information on available editions, translations undertaken, revisions planned, and ways of encouraging distribution and use of the Bible. Among other duties, the staff advise the national societies on problems of governmental control and restrictions and endeavor to safeguard the freedom of the circulation and use of the Bible. They also represent the Bible cause in relation to other international agencies, such as the World Council of Churches.

One of the most important activities of the United Bible Societies is the publication of a quarterly magazine, *The Bible Translator,* edited by a committee headed by Eugene A. Nida from 1949 to 1952 and by Wilfred J. Bradnock since January, 1953. This magazine provides fascinating "one world" reading. Its mailing list includes missionaries as well as missions, colleges, libraries, and linguistic institutes in all the capital cities and many of the farthest corners of the earth. In addition to feature articles by missionaries, professors, and philologists concerned with on-going Bible translations in Asian, Latin American, European, and African languages, this publication is a clearing house for questions on dialect problems from all over the world.

One questioner, working with a language in a culture where the father-son concept was weak, wanted to know how to deal with the Semitic idiom "Son of peace." Another translator who had faced this same problem in translating for the Navahos of southwestern United States responded that he had used "one who says peace" very successfully.

The translator in one Indian language of Latin America was so determined to "purify" the national language of contamination by Spanish that he confessed to a humorous blunder. He had used the phrase "a long-eared animal" instead of the familiar Spanish word *burro* for *ass.* The readers were very much puzzled when they read about Jesus' entry into Jerusalem. Since the word *burro* had not been used, they concluded that Jesus had ridden on a rabbit—the only other long-eared animal they knew.

Last year the United Bible Societies, through contributions from the American and British Bible Societies, gave mutual aid to their sister members in Korea and Japan. By 1953 the Korean society had printed 100,000 copies of the first modern Korean edition of the Bible, in Hankul spelling, for general circulation and distribution to orphanages, hospitals, and refugee and prisoner-of-war camps. The Korean editor, the Reverend Im Young Bin, a graduate of the Kaesong Mission High School in Seoul, Vanderbilt University in Nashville, Tennessee, and Southern Methodist University in Dallas, Texas, fought in our modern age the traditional fight of the Bible translators of old. Mr. Im once buried his manuscript in an old jar and fled with it from Seoul to Pusan to save it from the Communists. Another time four hundred pages of his manuscript were destroyed by the Communist bombing. Despite opposition, danger, and war, he completed his text in January, 1950, and then had to overcome all the problems of casting type in Tokyo to print in the new Korean characters. Hankul became the universal written language of Korea in 1948, and Mr. Im has been at work on the Hankul Bible since 1947.

In Japan 61,000 Bibles and 608,000 New Testaments were printed. It is estimated that some part of the Bible has now reached one out of every ten of the Japanese population. At Tokyo a board of revisers are at work on a new Bible, in the colloquial tongue.

At one of the choice corners in the heart of Manhattan, Fifty-seventh Street and Park Avenue, stands the American branch of the largest and oldest publishing business in the world. Through its doors have passed many of that great company of men and women who have adventured from the sierras of the Andes to the beaches of the Bering Straits—with and for a Book.

Over the reception desk of this great publishing house have passed correspondence and manuscripts in hundreds of tongues from peoples who owe their ability to write, their national unity, the very existence of their colorful postage stamps, to missionary-translators and statesmen. In giving hundreds of peoples their languages in writing, the missionaries replaced the primitive powers of oral communication by village runner and jungle drum with writing that could carry words around the world.

In the board room and at the library tables of this same building have sat, at one time or another, leaders and missionaries of every major Protestant denomination. The American Bible Society is undoubtedly one of the greatest interdenominational institutions in our country. Its one-goal purpose, its one-book business, is "the brotherhood of the Bible."

The American Bible Society was born in 1816 in the

present-day Board of Estimate room of the New York City Hall when the population of that city was barely one hundred thousand. It was founded in an era when church leadership and statesmanship were synonymous. Two of the many notable men present at the birth of the American Bible Society were James Fenimore Cooper, author of *The Last of the Mohicans,* and Dr. Lyman Beecher, father of all the famous Beechers, best known among them being Harriet, whose *Uncle Tom's Cabin* helped change American history.

Elias Boudinot, the first American Bible Society president, had, in 1789, been "president of the United States Congress Assembled." He had personally signed the peace treaty that ended the Revolutionary War. And this was the Congress, one of whose first resolutions was "to provide the people with Scripture." John Jay, the first Chief Justice of the United States Supreme Court, and Richard Varick, the second mayor of the city of New York, were also the American Bible Society's first vice-president and treasurer.

The Astor Place Bible House, erected in 1853, was then and for years afterward the showplace of New York. In front of its doors horse-drawn trams and carriages stopped daily to bring inland pioneers and sea-borne immigrants to gaze at and visit the first business building of New York to occupy an entire city block. Here the Bible or parts of it were printed and bound in one hundred and thirty-six languages. Many of the Gospels sold for as little as one cent.

In 1936 the Society moved to its first fire-proof building, the present attractive quarters on Park Avenue. From here is directed the work of a force of correspondents, office workers, volunteers, and colporteurs who have circulated, in the past year, 13,369,030 copies of the Scriptures to more than forty nations in five continents.

Here, too, daily informal tours are conducted through the building. Its first-floor murals depict life-size historic scenes from the Bible and illustrate the advent of the Book in the far corners of the earth. The second-floor library and board room contain show cases of rare and historic Bibles, or priceless remnants of them. Around the walls of this spacious room, from floor to ceiling, are nearly nineteen thousand different Bibles or parts of Bibles. Its vaults and safes contain treasured manuscript-Bibles and rare old first editions, displayed publicly on special occasions.

In the library reference room the telephone rings frequently. Day after day some few of New York's over eight million inhabitants and visitors want to know, "Where can I find this in the Bible?" Nationally famous magazine writers from all over the country and top flight public speakers from Wall Street to Knob Hill write in or call on Margaret T. Hills, who has been the library historian for nearly twenty years, and her associates for help in tracking down phrases, themes, and characters they vaguely remember having seen originally in their Bibles. All kinds of business and professional people from pharmaceutical advertisers to cosmetic copywriters call up for information. They ask for such things as "a list of drugs mentioned in the Bible" (there are none), or "biblical references on the beauty of the eye" (there are two).

People whose voices bristle with a hang-over of righteous indignation telephone to say abruptly, "We've just had an argument. Doesn't the Bible say . . ." At Christmas and Easter when the cathedrals of New York City ring with the music of the "Messiah" and "The Seven Last Words"; during theater seasons when the billboards of Broadway advertise plays like *Family Portrait* or *Many Mansions;* when any of the metropolitan art galleries exhibit El Greco's paintings or Connick's stained glass windows, people call upon the Bible House to settle points that trouble or attract them.

From the richly varied stocks of the Society's warehouse come the huge, handsome Bibles that supply America's pulpits as well as the Bibles of smaller sizes for personal use. Among these stocks are Bibles in Esperanto and in seventy-four foreign-language editions for the use of non-English-reading Americans.

Pioneering in printing for the blind since 1835, the American Bible Society now distributes thousands of the twenty-volume, ninety-pound editions of the Bible in Braille, and others in the Moon System, requiring fifty-eight volumes, each weighing more than a pound. The Society has supplied the blind with Bibles in thirty-six languages and systems of reading. There is also a ten-volume concordance in Braille. For those who cannot "see" with their fingers, the complete Bible has been produced on Talking Book records; one hundred and seventy ten-inch discs are required to record the Bible. Through solicitation of gifts from lovers of the Bible and friends of the blind, the Society offers each volume and each record for twenty-five cents, although they cost much more to produce. In many cases the books and records have been donated to those who are not only blind but cannot afford to pay for them.

In the making of a single edition of the Bible, thousands of yards of book cloth, gauze, and headbands; hundreds of bookbinders' needles and cones of thread; thousands of sets of end leaves, sheets of gold foil, and bundles of leather and tons of glue and paste, printer's ink, and paper are needed. For editions going to tropic and arctic countries, the Bible Society uses damp-proof and insect-resistant bindings and covers.

In many dramatic ways during World War II the Bible worked a mutual exchange of benefits. It enabled us, in spite of language barriers, to help our wounded allies who were rescued at sea and brought for healing to our shores. Its well known lessons of mercy gave motivation to Christian natives who assisted our men fallen on foreign beachheads and on mountain crags.

One day in a hospital in Richmond, Virginia, a Bible Society representative was making a visit in the wards. He spied among the patients a solitary brown-skinned marine. The boy had been taken wounded from a gunboat and was low, physically and mentally. Nobody could speak his language; he could speak not a word of English. He lay plucking the sheets feverishly in wretched isolation. The Bible Society representative, discovering from the medical officers where in the Philippine Islands the boy had come from, wired immediately to New York City for a copy of the one book he knew of in the Ilocano dialect. That book the boy read and read and read again, his courage restored, his isolation gone, proud that the

Book that belongs to the world belonged to him in the tongue of his homeland.

All these vital statistics and all this vast activity of translation, publication, and distribution that the American Bible Society carries on could only stem from a Book that is beloved by all the world.

The Bible is received and revered by peoples who are getting it for the first time, but how do we, who have taken it for granted for centuries, regard it today? We can buy it at book shops, in drug stores, at railroad terminal newsstands, in chain stores. We buy Bibles, Testaments, and smaller portions of the Bible at the rate of several million copies a year. Millions of the pupils who were enrolled last year in Sunday schools own Bibles.

Yet it is claimed, "The Bible is the unread best-seller," or "The Bible is the book nobody knows." How true these statements are, not even the American Bible Society really knows. Some interesting facts were gathered about our Bible-reading habits from a survey made in 1952 by Batten, Barton, Durstine & Osborn, Inc., a New York advertising agency. Ninety per cent of the people interviewed owned Bibles. Most Protestant homes have more than one. Ninety-five per cent of those owning Bibles said they read it "now and then;" 41 per cent of the Bible owners read it "at least once a week;" and 18 per cent read it "every single day."

American Bible Society executives have talked to teachers of Sunday and day schools and professors in colleges and universities about Bible reading among the young. "Rarely," say these instructors, "do we discover among our beginning students in religion, literature, history, and art any who know the biblical references with which these branches of knowledge are filled."

Another fact that interests the American Bible Society is that the legal opinions, paintings, and books of many of our greatest present-day judges (Learned Hand), artists (Jacob Epstein), and writers (Thomas Mann) reflect familiarity with the Bible's message. Mann spent fifteen years writing the tetralogy, *Joseph and His Brethren,* a story built around the last thirteen chapters of the book of *Genesis* in the Old Testament.

The Time Capsule was the most widely publicized stunt of the New York World's Fair in 1939. It was an eight-hundred-pound torpedo-shaped shell that the Westinghouse Electric and Manufacturing Company dreamed up and buried in Long Island to be dug up five thousand years later. A host of miscellaneous modern articles were put into it: a Lily Daché hat, golf balls, and approximately ten million words of microfilmed printed matter. Besides the published index of the contents of the Capsule, only one full-sized book went into it—the Bible.

When Dr. Francis C. Stifler, an American Bible Society secretary, called on the assistant to the president of the Westinghouse Electric and Manufacturing Company to ask him why the Bible had been placed in the Time Capsule, this is what Mr. Pendray said: "The Holy Bible, of all books familiar to us today, will most likely survive through the ages. Therefore, the Bible that we placed in the Time Capsule will be a sort of connecting link between the past, present, and future."

In little more than a decade the atomic bomb has put a question mark after more than the survival of the Time

Capsule; itself man's survival is now at stake. We need more than a connecting link between the past and future. We need a connecting link between the living present in our own land and the living present in all the countries around the world, if there is to be any future at all.

Science is of age in a streamlined world; human relations are still in their infancy. There is no other way to explain modern warfare and our inability to secure ourselves against war. We know more about making hydrogen bombs than we do about living with ourselves and with one another. We need the knowledge that Judge Learned Hand of New York has called "The Spirit of Liberty." In a speech before one hundred and fifty thousand newly naturalized citizens this jurist once said, "The spirit of liberty is the spirit of Him who, nearly two thousand years ago, taught mankind that lesson it has never learned, but has never quite forgotten: that there may be a kingdom where the least shall be heard and considered side by side with the greatest."

We have not outlived the messages of the Bible, which are as old as our own human needs, as modern as our world crisis. We still need, "Blessed are the peacemakers, for they shall be called sons of God. . . . If I speak in the tongues of men and of angels, but have not love, I am a noisy gong or a clanging cymbal. . . . So whatever you wish that men would do to you, do so to them. . . ."

Through day-by-day translation of these eternal truths into life, as well as into the many languages of the earth, we may find our way into the presence of God, bringing others with us. The way is open. Whatever our age or time, our nation or race, we may take our place in the great company of those who have lived by the instruction and songs of challenge to be found in the book of books, which is a monument to faith in God.

As it is written, "How beautiful are the feet of those who preach good news!" But they have not all heeded the gospel; for Isaiah says, "Lord, who has believed what he has heard from us?" So faith comes from what is heard, and what is heard comes by preaching of Christ.

But I ask, have they not heard? Indeed they have; for

> "Their voice has gone out to all
>   the earth,
> and their words to the ends of the
>   world."

> —*Romans* 10:15-18, from the
> Revised Standard Version

THE AUTHOR

VIOLET FRASER WOOD was born in Scotland and spent her first ten years in that country. Later she came with her family to Massachusetts, where her home was first in Methuen and then in Boston. At present she lives in Champaign-Urbana, Illinois, where she is an editorial writer on the staff of the University of Illinois Press. Her short stories and articles have appeared in national magazines and in the periodicals of nearly every major denomination in the United States and Canada. She is the author of *In the Direction of Dreams* and *So Sure of Life,* both publications of the Friendship Press. *Great Is the Company* has been translated into Spanish and Chinese.

THE ARTIST

RAFAEL PALACIOS, a former resident of Puerto Rico, is one of New York's busiest and most prolific artists. His successes in New York include a one-man show of gouaches, and participation in the First National Art Exhibition (representing Puerto Rico) and in the First Newspaper Artists' Show. He has also exhibited at the Atheneum and the University of Puerto Rico. Mr. Palacios has illustrated two other books for Friendship Press: *The Traded Twins* and *He Wears Orchids.*

THE FORMAT

The text of this book is set in Caledonia, a linotype face designed by W. A. Dwiggins, distinguished American designer, typographer, and illustrator. Caledonia belongs to the family of printing types called "modern face" by printers and is one of the most readable faces available.

The book was composed, printed, and bound by American Book–Stratford Press, of New York. Jackets and paper covers were printed by offset lithography by Triggs Color Printing Corporation, of New York. The text paper is Warren's Olde Style Laid.

Typographic design by Margery W. Smith
Binding by Louise E. Jefferson

Date Due

F Mar 26			
F Apr 9 R			
June 16			
D Nov. 16			